Whispering Ghosts

The Laidlaw Reading Program LEVEL 9

William Eller

Kathleen B. Hester

S. Elizabeth Davis

Thomas J. Edwards

Roger Farr

Jack W. Humphrey

DayAnn McClenathan

Nancy Lee Roser

Elizabeth M. Ryan

Ann Myra Seaver

Marian Alice Simmons

Margaret Wittrig

Patricia J. Cianciolo, *Children's literature*

David W. Reed, *Linguistics*

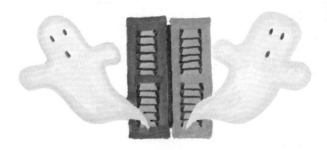

LAIDLAW BROTHERS • PUBLISHERS

A Division of Doubleday & Company, Inc.

RIVER FOREST, ILLINOIS

Palo Alto, California

New York, New York

Atlanta, Georgia

Toronto, Canada

Dallas, Texas

Acknowledgments

Addison-Wesley Publishing Company for "Kiya, the Gull." Adapted from KIYA THE GULL © 1969, by Fen Lasell, an Addisonian Press Book, by permission of Addison-Wesley Publishing Company.

Association for Childhood Education International for the poem "Fuzzy Wuzzy, Creepy Crawly" from SUNG UNDER THE SILVER UMBRELLA by Lillian Schulz Vanada. Reprinted by permission of the Association for Childhood Education International, 3615 Wisconsin Avenue, N. W., Washington, D. C. Copyright © 1935 by the Association.

Atheneum Publishers, Inc. for the first, second, and last stanza of the poem "Me Myself and I" from THERE IS NO RHYME FOR SILVER. Copyright © 1962 by Eve Merriam. From THERE IS NO RHYME FOR SILVER. Used by permission of Atheneum Publishers.

Childrens Press for "The Trouble with Horses." Adapted from THE TROUBLE WITH HORSES, by Dorothy Halle Seligman. A Golden Gate Book published by Childrens Press of Chicago. Copyright © 1971. Used by permission of Childrens Press.

(Acknowledgments continue on page 311.)

Project Director: Ralph J. Cooke
Senior Editor: Helen W. Crane
Senior Staff Editor: Marilyn L. Maples
Editor: Suzanne Callahan
Production Director: LaVergne G. Niequist
Production Associate: Angela Zabransky
Art Director: Gloria Muczynski
Art Consultant: Donald Meighan
Cover Art: Donald Charles

Illustrators: Angela Adams, Corinne and Robert Borja, Ted Carr, Ralph Creasman, Beatrice Darwin, Pat Doyle, Mike Eagle, Len Ebert, John Faulkner, Jack Haesly, Hilary Hayton, Orin Kincade, Dick Kramer, Ron LeHew, Robert Masheris, Donald Meighan, Tak Murakami, Jan Pyk, Joe Rogers, Jack Wallen

Photographers: Dr. E. R. Degginger (pp. 226 top, 228, 229, 231); DeWys (p. 31); Grant Heilman (pp. 227 top right, 230); John R. Kennedy/Free Lance Photographers Guild, Inc. (pp. 192, 193); Steve McCutcheon (p. 243); Michael Sullivan (p. 57); Eileen Tanson/Tom Stack (pp. 226 bottom, 227 top left, 227 bottom)

ISBN 0-8445-3425-1

Copyright © 1976 by
Laidlaw Brothers, Publishers
A Division of Doubleday & Company, Inc.

Contents

All's Well That Ends Well

How and Why

3

4

A Beautiful World

Quick Thinking

No, No, Rosina

The time of day that Rosina liked best was half past three in the morning. That was the time when all the shouting started in her family.

"Up!" called Mama. "Everybody up. Breakfast will be ready before you are dressed."

"Hit the deck," said Luigi.

"Rise and shine," said Carlo. "Rise and shine."

"Up!" shouted Papa. "We have work to do."

"And may you have good luck and a good catch today," said Mama.

As long as Rosina could remember, she had
wanted to go with her father and brothers on their
fishing boat. All through the winter they sailed from
San Francisco Bay in search of crabs.

Far out in the ocean, Rosina's family had their
own wire traps—crab pots they were called. Orange-
colored floats showed where the crab pots lay, deep
on the bottom of the ocean.

Rosina had seen the wire traps and the orange-colored floats lying on the wharf. But she had never been allowed to go to sea with her father and brothers. Every time she had asked, Papa had said No.

"Please let me go!" begged Rosina. "I could help!"

And Papa always said, "No, no, Rosina. It is not a question of helping. I have enough helpers. I have your uncle. And when there is no school, I have Luigi and Carlo."

Rosina thought about Luigi and Carlo, lucky big brothers who went with Papa in search of crabs. But Rosina, who was named for a beautiful fishing boat, had only been allowed on the deck of her father's boat. She had never once been to sea.

Now, in less than a month, Rosina would be back in school. So she asked the same old question one more time. "Papa, can I go?"

Papa shouted, "You ask again?" He raised his arms in the air. "The little one asks again."

"But when Luigi and Carlo are gone, I'm lonely," said Rosina.

"Stop feeling sorry for yourself," said Luigi. "Next month we'll be back in school. You'll see your friends every day, so you won't be lonely."

"But what about right now? Please say Yes," begged Rosina.

"A woman in a fishing boat brings bad luck," cried Papa.

"But she's such a small woman," said Carlo. "Maybe it wouldn't matter if she came with us."

"No," said Luigi. "A fishing boat is no place for a girl."

While she ate her breakfast, Rosina thought about what her father and brothers had said. This time when she had asked to go, Papa had talked about bad luck. But he hadn't said No.

After Rosina had eaten, she slipped on a warm sweater and went outside. The fog was so heavy that the glow of lights in the windows could hardly be seen. Farther down the street was Fisherman's Wharf, where the fishing boats were tied up.

Suddenly Rosina knew what she must do. She must show Papa that she wouldn't bring bad luck. Quickly, quietly, she would go aboard the *Santa Rosa.*

Rosina pulled her sweater tightly around her and ran toward the wharf. There, in the early morning fog, the *Santa Rosa* waited, bumping against the ladder that led down from the wharf.

Rosina went aboard and looked around for a place to hide.

On the deck near her feet was the big square wooden crab box, ready for the day's catch. An old overcoat hung behind the cabin door—just what Rosina needed! She hid behind the overcoat, hoping no one would see her.

SANTA ROSA II

15

Two Kinds of Luck

Soon Rosina could hear noises on the wharf. Fishermen were calling to each other.

"Where's Tony today?" shouted one man.

Rosina heard her uncle's answer. "He has engine trouble. He can't go out today."

Just then Papa and Uncle came aboard.

"Warm up the engine," shouted Papa.

Rosina felt the deck of the *Santa Rosa* move under her feet.

Her heart pounded when she heard Luigi and Carlo come into the cabin. She didn't dare move for fear they would see her and tell Papa. Finally, after what seemed like hours, her brothers left the cabin and went up on deck.

"All ready," shouted Papa as he slowly steered the boat away from shore and into San Francisco Bay. Soon the glow of the early morning sun could be seen shining on the water. Papa steered the *Santa Rosa* under the Golden Gate Bridge and headed for the ocean.

Finally Papa shouted, "There's our trapline!"

The waves splashed against the side of the boat as the men brought the first crab pot on board.

"There're lots of crabs," said Luigi.

All this time Rosina had been listening from her hiding place in the cabin. This was what she had been waiting for. "Guess who's here!" she said as she jumped on deck.

"A stowaway on board!" shouted Carlo.

"It's a little crab named Rosina," said Luigi.

Papa opened his mouth to shout, but no words came. He lifted his hands toward the sky and then held his head. He was very angry.

Rosina spoke loudly so she could be heard above the noise of the wind and the splashing of the water. "I wanted to show you that I wouldn't bring bad luck."

"I will talk to you later about this!" shouted Papa.

He turned to Uncle. "Call shore and have someone tell Mama that we have Rosina."

He looked at Luigi and Carlo. "Why do you stand doing nothing? We have work to do."

Luigi emptied the crabs from the wire pot into the wooden box.

"There are lots of crabs," said Carlo. "But they look small."

"They are small," said Uncle. "Not one crab is big enough to keep."

"See what has happened," cried Papa. "There should have been at least twenty big crabs."

"Perhaps the next pot will be full of big ones," said Carlo.

Uncle tossed the little crabs back into the ocean. Then Luigi dropped the crab pot into the water. It landed with a splash and sank to the bottom of the sea, far below the orange-colored float.

Rosina looked out over the water as her father steered the boat alongside the next float. She could see many other fishing boats, ten or twenty of them, all working with their own crab pots. Birds flew overhead and a great wave splashed against the side of the *Santa Rosa.*

Rosina tasted salt from the water. She looked back to see the pink glow of the sunrise over San Francisco.

Rosina wondered what Luigi and Carlo would find in the second crab pot. Perhaps Papa would forget to be angry if there was a good catch of fine, big crabs.

When the crab pot was brought on board, Rosina looked into the wire cage. Her heart sank. Only a few small crabs were inside.

Papa groaned loudly. "Look at them! Not one crab is big enough to keep."

22

Carlo tossed the little crabs back into the ocean. "Look!" he shouted. "I see a bottle splashing about in the water. It's coming this way."

Luigi used a hand net to lift the bottle from the water. "There's a note inside," he said. He pulled out a small roll of paper.

"I am a fisherman's son," he read. "I live in Monterey. Will you write to me? I want to be your friend."

"Does the note say anything else?" asked Carlo.

"Only the boy's name and age," answered Luigi as he put the piece of paper back in the bottle.

"So. We return home with a catch of one friend. But that's about all." Papa was still angry. "Nothing much today," he said. "Nothing much at all."

Papa steered the boat on through the sea to the third float. When Luigi and Carlo brought up the pot, Uncle and Papa quickly looked over the crabs.

"These are better," said Uncle.

"Twenty-three big ones!" shouted Papa.

There were many large crabs in the other traps as well. All morning the men worked. The big crabs went into the square wooden box and the little ones were tossed back into the sea. Each time, the crab pot was dropped over the side, and it sank deep in the water beneath its float.

"Tomorrow our crab pots will be full again," said Rosina. "We have had good luck today."

Papa didn't answer.

Carlo spoke softly. "Look at the crabs, Papa. We have had a good catch after all. The little one has brought no bad luck."

Lucky Rosina

When the last pot was raised, Carlo looked inside and shouted, "Another stowaway!"

"An octopus," said Rosina. "We can have it for supper."

Carlo lifted the octopus in the hand net and held it up for Papa to see.

"Today we caught hundreds and hundreds of crabs," said Rosina. "And an octopus. And we found a note in a bottle."

She thought of the boy from Monterey. "How old is the boy who wrote the note?" she asked.

"He's twelve," said Luigi.

"Then Carlo must answer it," she said.

"Already Rosina, the stowaway, gives the orders," said Papa. "She hides in the cabin of our boat and tells us what to do. I, only I, give orders around here."

He pointed to Carlo and said, "Yes, you will write to the boy. Wish him good luck and good fishing."

When the fog had cleared away and the sun was high in the sky, Papa turned the *Santa Rosa* toward shore. He carefully steered the boat into Fisherman's Wharf.

Rosina knew that she would never be allowed to go aboard the *Santa Rosa* again. This was a day she would always remember. She would enjoy it to the last minute. She waved at the other fishing boats and at a party boat as it passed.

When they reached home, Papa talked with Rosina. At the end of his talk, he said, "And now you will speak with Mama."

"I'm sorry," said Rosina. "I never meant to worry you. I won't go away again without telling you first. Not even with Papa and Luigi and Carlo."

"Good," said Mama. "Now we will fix the octopus for dinner and forget what you have done."

Rosina didn't really forget. She was dreaming of crabs and the salt smell of the sea when the alarm clock went off the next morning.

She jumped out of bed, turned off the alarm, and quickly got dressed.

"Rise and shine," shouted Rosina. "Hit the deck, everybody. Up, Carlo! Up, Luigi!"

"No, no, Rosina," said Carlo. "Luigi and I don't have to get up until sunrise. We're going to stay ashore today and help Cousin Tony fix his engine."

Rosina understood what Carlo said. It meant she would be by herself again today. Already she felt a little lonely.

"Cheer up," laughed Carlo. "You're sure lucky today. Mama said you're allowed to go on the *Santa Rosa* with Papa."

Rosina was excited. She put on Luigi's raincoat. She put on Carlo's rain hat.

Papa was shouting.

"Fix a good lunch, Mama," he said. "Fix a good lunch for Lucky Rosina and me!"

Shore

Play on the seashore
And gather up shells,
Kneel in the deep sands
Digging wells.

Run on the rocks
Where the seaweed slips,
Watch the waves
And the beautiful ships.

Mary Britton Miller

31

The Middle Muddle

At lunch Mike began making tracks in the potatoes with his fork.

"Mike!" said Mrs. Muddle. "You're too old to play with your food."

"Look at Susie," said Mike. "She's doing the same thing with her fork."

"That's different," said his mother. "Susie's only a baby."

Mike's older brother, Steve, pushed back his chair. "May I be excused?" he asked. "The fellows will be here soon, and I have to get some last-minute stuff packed for our weekend campout."

His mother nodded. "You're excused," she said. "By the way, Steve, be sure to take along a heavy sweater. You know how cold it can get on Indian Mountain."

Mike laid his fork on his plate. "Can I go with Steve and the other kids?" he asked.

"No," said his mother. "You're too young to go camping overnight."

"Aw, please, Mom," begged Mike. "I never get to do the stuff that Steve does."

Mrs. Muddle sighed, "I'm sorry, but I couldn't even consider it."

Now it was Mike's turn to sigh. Everybody considered him either too small or too big to do the things he wanted. It wasn't much fun being the middle kid in the family.

That afternoon Steve left for Indian Mountain, and Mother took Susie upstairs for her nap. Mike decided to weed the tomato patch that he had planted beside the house. He pulled one weed, and then another. Finally he grew tired of weeding. He sat down and just looked at the tomato plants.

"Boy," he thought to himself. "This sure isn't a very exciting afternoon."

Down at the end of the street, three men in overalls were digging a hole. Mike stood up and brushed the dirt from his hands and knees.

"I can weed a tomato patch any old day," he thought as he walked to the corner. "But it isn't every day that I can watch men digging a hole right in the middle of my street!"

"Hello there, young fellow," said a red-haired workman. Mike remembered seeing him when the sidewalk was fixed last spring.

"This is Mike, the middle Muddle," the red-haired man told his friends. "Too bad he's not wearing overalls. We'd put him to work."

"That's right, Muddle," joked one of the men.

"Please quit teasing me about my name," said Mike quietly. His face turned a glowing red.

"We didn't really mean to hurt your feelings," said the third workman. "We're just having a little fun. In fact, we tease each other all the time."

Mike smiled. "I guess that makes sense," he said. "Say, does that kitten belong to one of you?"

"What kitten?" asked the red-haired workman.

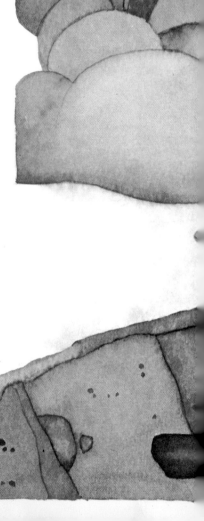

"Over there," said Mike.

"Where? I don't see any . . ." The man looked around just in time to see the tip of a tail disappear into a narrow pipe.

"It's a gray kitten with white paws and a white tip on its tail," said Mike.

"A water pipe is no place for a cat!" said the workman. "But getting it out should be simple."

"Here, kitty," called Mike. "Here, kitty, kitty."

From deep inside the pipe where the kitten had disappeared came a tiny "Meow."

"We've got to get that cat out," shouted one of the men. "The water's going to be turned on at two o'clock!"

The red-haired man looked at his watch. "We've got less than twenty minutes," he said.

Mike could hear the kitten's frightened meowing. "Don't let them turn on the water," he cried out in alarm. "We can't let the kitten drown! We have to get it out!"

"Nobody wants the kitten to drown," said the red-haired man. "If there's any possible way, we'll get it out."

"But what if the kitten's stuck in there?" asked Mike. "We might need more time. Couldn't you call the water company and tell them not to turn on the water?"

"That makes sense," explained the man. "But it's not that simple. There's a telephone at the water company, but the one at the pumping station is out of order."

"We'd better quit talking and think of something else—fast!" said another workman. "Time is running out for us."

By this time a group of people had gathered. The kitten was meowing, the people were watching, and the minutes were slipping by.

A workman lay flat on the ground and put his hand into the pipe.

"Can you reach the kitten?" asked Mike.

"No," sighed the man. "It's just not possible. My arm's too big. It scrapes against the sides of the pipe."

Another workman tried to get the kitten, but he couldn't reach far enough into the narrow pipe.

"Let the boy try," shouted someone in the group. "His arm's thin, so it won't scrape the sides of the pipe."

Mike looked into the narrow pipe and saw two bright eyes shining in the dark.

He put his arm into the pipe and wiggled his fingers. Suddenly he felt soft fur touch his fingertips. Mike moved his hand very slowly so he wouldn't frighten the kitten. He was able to get two fingers around one leg. Very carefully he pulled the kitten toward him. It hadn't been stuck at all! It had been too frightened to come out!

"Hurry, Mike," called the red-haired man. "If we don't get this pipe hooked up, half the neighborhood will be flooded."

"I've got it!" shouted Mike. A loud cheer came from the group when he held up the kitten.

"You're OK, kitty," said Mike as he hugged the frightened cat against his sweater.

The men quickly hooked up the pipe. The very moment they finished, water could be heard pouring through it.

"Whew!" said the red-haired man. "That was a close call. We almost had a neighborhood flood."

He turned to Mike and said, "Thanks to you, the pipe was hooked up on time."

That was the moment when Mike thought of something. If he had been the littlest Muddle, he would have been at home taking a nap. If he had been the biggest Muddle, he would have been camping on Indian Mountain.

Mike hugged the kitten close to him. "Know what?" he whispered. "It's a good thing I'm the middle Muddle."

Holiday Upset

This was Ginger's first year to march in the Fourth of July parade. How she was looking forward to it! She was so excited she could hardly wait.

Ginger's Brownie dress was washed and ironed, ready for the holiday. Her brown shoes were polished so brightly she could almost see herself in them. Her socks were on the dresser near the bed.

Her father was a city fireman. This year it was his turn to drive the fire engine in the holiday parade. Her mother had pressed his uniform, and Ginger had helped him polish the gold buttons.

"Thanks," he had said when they had finished. "These shiny buttons make my uniform look just like new."

On the afternoon before the parade, Ginger went
down to the firehouse to help polish the huge fire
engine. It seemed as though she had hardly started
when her father said, "Time for you to go home, dear.
Your mother will want you to watch the twins while
she prepares dinner."

"Aren't you coming?" asked Ginger.

"I'll be along in a moment," replied her father.
"I'm going to give the engine a final check. I want to
be sure everything's ready for the parade."

"OK, Dad," said Ginger. She left the firehouse
and hurried toward home.

Soon Ginger reached the walk that led to the front porch. She didn't notice the toy truck that one of the twins had left on the top step. As she stepped on the toy its wheels rolled forward. Ginger tried to grab the porch railing, but she couldn't keep from falling. The full weight of her body came down on one foot!

"Ouch!" she cried.

Ginger's mother ran to the porch when she heard her daughter's cry of pain. "What happened? Are you hurt?"

"It's my foot. I don't think I can walk!" replied Ginger. She grabbed the railing and tried to pull herself up.

"Keep your weight off that foot," said her mother. "I'll help you into the house."

Ginger put an arm around her mother and hopped inside. She was glad to sit down and rest her foot. She tried not to cry when her mother took off her shoe and sock and placed a pillow under her foot. But the pain was so great that tears flooded her eyes.

"Look at that huge lump!" cried Ginger. "It's turning black and blue."

"Let's have Doctor Tower check your foot," replied her mother. "Don't worry. He'll tell us what to do."

A short time later Doctor Tower arrived. After looking at Ginger's foot, he said, "That's quite a lump, but nothing is broken. You'll have to keep your weight off that foot for a few days."

"Do you mean I can't march in the parade?" cried Ginger, forgetting for a moment how her foot ached.

"I'm afraid not," replied Doctor Tower kindly.

"But there won't be another holiday for months," sighed Ginger. "And I'll have to wait a whole year before the Fourth of July comes again."

"I know how disappointed you must be, but it won't be possible for you to march tomorrow," said Doctor Tower.

The doctor started out the door. "Ginger's foot may ache for awhile," he told her mother. "But she'll be fine in a few days."

"Thank you for coming, Doctor Tower," said Ginger's mother. After checking to see if Ginger needed anything, she hurried to the kitchen to prepare dinner.

Dad Saves the Day

The Fourth of July was a clear, bright day. By nine o'clock everyone had finished breakfast. Ginger's dad had on his dark blue uniform. Her mother and the twins were preparing to walk to the corner where they could watch the parade.

Lonely and disappointed, Ginger sat by the window with her foot resting on the pillow. Several times, when no one was looking, she put weight on her aching foot. But each time, the pain was so bad that she finally gave up.

Suddenly a car horn sounded outside. Some of Dad's friends had arrived to take him to the firehouse.

"I'll wave when we go by the corner," he called to Ginger's mother. "And I'll blow the siren for the twins."

He put his arm around Ginger's shoulder. "Maybe I'll see you a little later, too," he said. Then he gave her a hug and dashed out the front door.

Ginger wondered what her father had meant. It didn't make sense. He wouldn't see her in the parade. Surely he wouldn't tease her when he knew how disappointed she was. When the parade was over, there was going to be a party at the firehouse. Ginger knew she wouldn't see her father until much later in the day.

She picked up her drawing pencils and tried to forget about the parade. She decided to draw a funny clown, using the brightest pencils she had. But it was no use! Nothing could keep her from being disappointed. Nothing could make her forget how excited she had been while helping polish the fire engine. And nothing could make her forget what had happened when she had arrived home yesterday.

"If I had only seen that old toy," thought Ginger. "If I had only grabbed the porch railing!"

The phone rang and Ginger's mother dashed to answer it. A moment later she came into the room with Ginger's Brownie uniform over her arm.

"That was your dad," she said. "You're going to be in the parade after all! Hurry, so you'll be ready when he gets here."

Ginger dropped the paper and pencils. "How can I?" she asked, her eyes glowing with happiness. "My foot still aches."

"You'll see," was all her mother would say.

"What about my shoes and socks?" asked Ginger.

"You can go barefoot," replied Mother. "It would be too painful to put on a sock and shoe. Besides, you won't be doing any walking."

Before long her father arrived. He grabbed Ginger in his arms and started toward the door. "You're going to ride in the fire engine with me," he explained. "I had to check with the Chief first to make sure it was OK. I didn't want to disappoint you. So here we go!"

Ginger was too excited to notice the pain when her foot scraped against the railing as Dad carried her down the porch steps.

He lifted her into the fire engine. Someone had even thought to put a pillow on the floor so Ginger could rest her foot.

"Push that button," said Dad as he steered the huge engine into the street.

Ginger pushed the button, and the siren rang out loud and clear!

Her face glowed with happiness as she waved to her mother and the twins. Then she and Dad drove off. It was going to be a great holiday after all!

I Love a Parade

I love a parade,
The tramping of feet,
I love ev'ry beat
I hear of a drum.

I love a parade,
When I hear a band
I just want to stand
and cheer as they come.

Ted Koehler

57

ONE MORE CHANCE

The hills were touched with warm, spring green, but even the sunshine all about him didn't make Red happy. He was carrying a lunch to Mill Woods, where his father was helping a neighbor, Mr. Mill, clear some land. Red's little sister, Anne, was hopping along beside him.

"I want you to hold my hand, Red," she demanded. "The ground's rocky. I might fall!"

Red looked at his little sister and frowned. Any other day he might have enjoyed Anne's company, but not today. She was the cause of all his trouble!

Anne had forgotten the bump on her head. That morning she had tripped over Red's foot and had fallen against the door. She had forgotten her screams of pain that had caused her parents to come running. But Red hadn't forgotten.

He could still see his mother taking Anne into her arms and drying the little girl's tears. He could still hear Anne saying, "Red knocked me down, Mommy. He did it on purpose!" Most of all, Red could still see the frown on his father's face.

Anne had held her head and yelled again, "He tripped me on purpose, Daddy! He tripped me and made me fall!"

"You tripped her?" his father had demanded in a strange voice.

Red had looked at his parents, not knowing what to say. The huge lump on Anne's head had frightened him badly.

"We were playing," he had explained. "She fell over my foot. I didn't—"

"He did it on purpose," Anne had screamed. "Red hurt me, Daddy!"

Red's father had frowned again. "I promised Mr. Mill I'd be over early to help him clear away some dead trees. You feed the cattle, Red, and stay around home and make yourself useful. I hope then you'll realize that it's dangerous to trip people—most of all a little girl like Anne."

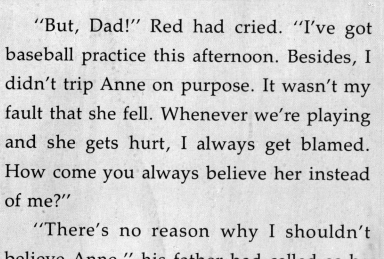

"But, Dad!" Red had cried. "I've got baseball practice this afternoon. Besides, I didn't trip Anne on purpose. It wasn't my fault that she fell. Whenever we're playing and she gets hurt, I always get blamed. How come you always believe her instead of me?"

"There's no reason why I shouldn't believe Anne," his father had called as he hurried out the door. "Feed the cattle, Son. Missing one baseball practice won't put you off the team."

"Run, Anne!" Red had begged. "Tell Dad that I didn't trip you on purpose. Tell him it was an accident."

Tears were still bright in Anne's eyes. She shook her head. "You stuck out your big old foot, and you know it."

"You'd better feed the cattle," his mother had said in a troubled voice.

With his head down, Red had turned and walked away silently.

All morning, he had stayed away from Anne. Noon came, and their mother had sent them to Mill Woods with a hot lunch for their father.

"Do I have to take Anne?" Red had asked. "If she gets a scrape or a scratch, she'll blame me, and I'll be in more trouble. Mom, why can't Dad realize that everything that happens to Anne isn't my fault?"

"It's not always easy for people to understand one another," his mother had answered. "Your father was in a hurry this morning. All he could see was the lump on Anne's head. He thought you had tripped her. That's the reason he was so upset."

Red supposed that his mother was right. What she had said made sense. Just the same, it was Anne's fault that he was missing baseball practice.

Almost Too Late

After he and Anne had left the house, Red had tried to explain that being hurt on purpose was different from being hurt by accident. But she had touched the bump on her head and said, "It still hurts." Red had soon realized that his sister didn't understand, so he walked along silently.

"Let's play follow-the-leader," said Anne, hopping along beside her brother.

Red just frowned. "If we play follow-the-leader and you get a scratch, you'll blame me. So I'm going to leave you alone. You can play by yourself, and walk by yourself, and do everything by yourself."

"You're mean!" cried Anne. "But I don't care. Anyhow, I can run faster than you can."

Without waiting for an answer, she dashed off toward a nearby pasture. "Beat you to Daddy," she called over her shoulder.

Red watched as she bent her small body and started to crawl under the wire fence. Suddenly he realized where she was going—into the pasture where Mr. Mill kept Solomon, his prize bull.

"Don't, Anne!" he screamed in alarm. "Don't go into Solomon's pasture!" But it was too late. Anne was already on the other side of the fence.

"I'll beat you to Daddy," she called again, running as fast as she could.

Red dropped the lunch and ran after her. Even though the huge bull was not in sight, Red knew how dangerous Solomon could be. More than once he had appeared out of nowhere and had charged at anyone who had dared to come into the pasture.

Red crawled under the fence and quickly looked around. There, behind a clump of low-growing brush, he saw the thing he feared—Solomon's big horns!

Just then Red spotted his father. He was within sight of the pasture but separated from Anne by another fence.

"Dad!" he screamed. "Help! Help Anne!" But his father was too far away to help.

Red could hear the sound of breaking branches as the big bull pushed through the undergrowth. Then came a deep roar and the thunder of hoofs. The bull began to charge.

Red grabbed Anne by the shoulder and pulled her across the ground. With all his might, he pushed her under the fence, out of reach of the charging bull. The thundering hoofs were not far behind as Red rolled after his sister.

The children lay on the ground, breathless and
frightened. They were separated from the bull by
the wire fence, and they were safe at last.

Red was still breathless and Anne was crying when their father and Mr. Mill arrived. The men were short of breath, too, and both were frightened.

"Are you all right?" asked Red's dad, putting his hand on the boy's shoulder.

"I guess so," answered Red in a shaky voice. "But that was a close call!"

"My knee's scratched," cried Anne as her father held her close.

"You'll be fine," he said, "thanks to Red."

"There's blood on my knee," she screamed. "See the blood? Red knocked me down on purpose, Daddy."

"Of course he did it on purpose," answered her father. "If he hadn't, you'd have more than scratches! Red saved your life, Anne, and it's time you learned what doing something on purpose really means."

She pulled away from him and stopped crying.

"You mean hurting me on purpose was good?" she asked.

"This time it was," he answered. "You got hurt when Red tried to help you. So don't blame him. Hurting you on purpose was good."

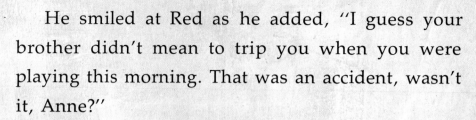

He smiled at Red as he added, "I guess your brother didn't mean to trip you when you were playing this morning. That was an accident, wasn't it, Anne?"

Anne nodded silently. Then she turned toward Red. "You'll still play with me, won't you?"

Red gave his little sister a hug.

"Is it too late to get to baseball practice, Son?" asked his father. "I could drive you there."

"We'll make it, Dad," Red said happily. And the three of them headed across the field.

Why the Bat Flies at Night

Most people know that the bat sleeps all day and flies only at night. But this was not always true. In a faraway time, in a faraway place, the bat also flew in the daylight.

Long, long ago, the bat was flying about in the sunshine. Suddenly a hawk appeared out of nowhere and joined him in flight.

"Friend Bat," called the hawk, trying to make his voice sound pleasant. "I've been searching for you for the past few months."

"Well, well," said the bat. "What need do you have of me?"

"There's going to be a war between the birds and the beasts," replied the hawk. "All the birds would like you to join forces with them."

"Me!" squeaked the bat, trying to act surprised. "There must be some mistake. Why should I join the birds in a war against the beasts? I am not a bird, and on no account will I join the birds. Now, if you'll excuse me, I must run along."

With that, the bat sank to the ground, folded his wings, and ran across the grass on his four feet.

"What a fool I am!" said the hawk as he continued his flight. "I have made a mistake. The bat is not a bird at all. Indeed, the bat belongs to the kingdom of the beasts. Still, I wonder . . ."

The bat went on until he found himself deep in the woods. He was out of breath and too weak to go any farther, so he stopped to rest beneath some oak trees. The heat from the afternoon sun was great, but the shade of the oak trees felt pleasant.

While the bat was resting, he heard a noise nearby. A jackal came out of the underbrush and sat down beside him.

"Good afternoon, Friend Bat," said the jackal pleasantly. "How lucky you are to escape the heat and rest in the shade of these oak trees! And how lucky I am to have finally caught sight of you. For the past few months I've searched everywhere for you."

"Well, well," sighed the bat. "What need do you have of me?"

"There's going to be a war between the beasts and the birds," replied the jackal. "All the beasts would like you to join forces with them."

"Me!" squeaked the bat. "There must be some mistake. Why should I join the beasts in a war against the birds? I am not a beast, and on no account will I join the beasts. Now, if you'll excuse me, I must continue my flight."

With that, the bat unfolded his wings and sailed high above the oak trees.

"What a fool I am!" thought the jackal to himself. "I have made a mistake. The bat is not a beast at all. Indeed, the bat belongs to the bird kingdom. Still, I wonder. . . "

From that moment on, the bat never ran again for fear the jackal would see him. In fact, his legs became so weak that they were of no use to him. And he never dared to fly in the daylight for fear the hawk would see him.

So from that time to this, the bat has stayed hidden in the daytime. He flies only at night when the hawk is fast asleep.

Why the Sun and the Moon Live in the Sky

Long, long ago the sun and the water were friends. They both lived on the earth in good will and happiness. Quite often the sun paid a visit to the water, but the water never went to visit the sun. As a result, the sun thought the water was not polite. He wondered why the water never came to see him.

"What reason do you have for not coming to visit me?" asked the sun. "I have invited you many times. You would be welcome! Your people would be welcome also."

"Alas!" replied the water. "Each time you invited me I had to refuse. Your house is too small. If my people and I paid you a visit, we would surely drive you out. The results would be terrible! If you want me to visit, you must build a new house. But I warn you, it must be very large indeed. When my people are gathered together, they take up much room."

The sun considered what the water had said and agreed to build a house big enough for the water and all his people.

Soon afterwards, the sun returned home. His wife, the moon, welcomed him with a broad smile.

"I have invited the water to come for a visit," he told her. "He refused to come until I agreed to build a house big enough to hold him and his people."

"Not once during all these years has the water paid us a visit," replied the moon. "I will be delighted to see him. We must begin at once to prepare our new house."

The very next day the sun and the moon began to build the house. They worked rapidly, and not long afterwards it was ready for the visitors.

When the water arrived, his servant knocked on the door. "Water wishes to know whether it is safe to enter," he said politely.

The sun smiled broadly and answered, "Yes, indeed! Tell my friend he is welcome. The moon and I will be delighted to have his company."

So the water started to enter the house. And with him came the fish and the beasts of the water kingdom.

Soon the water was knee-deep, and the servant once again went to the sun. "Water wishes to know whether it is still safe for more of his people to enter," he said politely.

The sun and the moon also wanted to be polite. They smiled pleasantly and replied, "Yes, by all means, continue to enter."

The water flowed rapidly, bringing a parade of fish and beasts into the house.

Not long afterwards, the water had nearly reached the ceiling. Again the servant called out, "Water wishes to know whether more of his people are welcome."

The sun and the moon still wanted to be polite, even though they were no longer delighted with their visitors. They tried to smile broadly and said, "Yes."

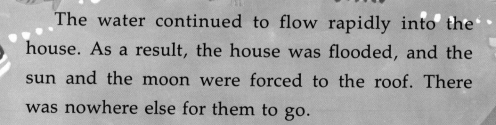

The water continued to flow rapidly into the house. As a result, the house was flooded, and the sun and the moon were forced to the roof. There was nowhere else for them to go.

The water did not stop when it reached the ceiling. No, indeed! Instead, the water, together with the fish and the other beasts, flowed over the rooftop.

The servant was no longer able to talk with the sun and the moon. They had been forced far into the sky, where they have remained to this very day.

How the Necklace Was Found

There was once a garden that belonged to a beautiful princess. The treetops in the garden were filled with monkeys.

One monkey was quite vain and thought she was prettier than all the others. In fact, she was so vain that she spent a great amount of time looking at herself in a mirror.

VAIN MONKEY: (*Holding the mirror*) Look at me! Just look at me! See how pretty I am. I'm the prettiest monkey in the whole garden.

FIRST MONKEY: Why do you say that? You look no different than the rest of us.

VAIN MONKEY: That's not true! Take another look. I am the prettiest because I wear flower blossoms behind my ear.

SECOND MONKEY: Whoever heard of a monkey wearing flower blossoms! Look in your mirror and see how silly you are. Anyway, we'd much rather watch the beautiful princess and her maid. Here they come now.

Each afternoon the princess came to swim in a stream that flowed through the garden. But first she always took off her necklace of beautiful pearls and handed it to the maid.

PRINCESS: It is your duty to guard this pearl necklace. You know that it is my greatest treasure.

MAID: Yes, your Highness. Never fear. I will guard the necklace with my life.

PRINCESS: I know you will. You have never failed me.

MAID: Thank you, your Highness.

PRINCESS: Because the heat of the sun is so great, I may swim in the stream the rest of the afternoon.

MAID: Whatever you wish, your Highness.

High up in a treetop, the vain monkey spotted the pearl necklace.

VAIN MONKEY: (*To herself*) Oh, I wish I could wear that pearl necklace. How beautiful I would look. If the maid is careless, I might be able to steal it.

The princess spent a great amount of time swimming in the stream. As a result, her maid grew tired and fell asleep in the shade of a tree. Thus, the pearl necklace was left unguarded.

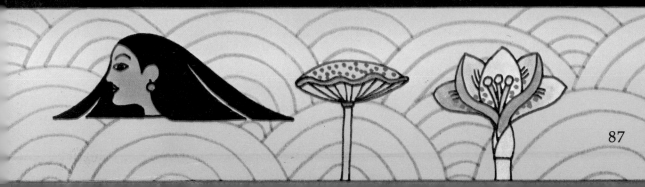

VAIN MONKEY: (*To herself*) Aha! The maid has fallen asleep. Now I will have a chance to take the wonderful treasure.

The vain monkey jumped down from the treetop and grabbed the necklace. Nobody noticed as she hid it beside the mirror in the hollow of a tree. In a short while the maid woke up.

MAID: Oh my goodness! The necklace is gone! I must find it quickly! Before the princess finishes her swim.

PRINCESS: (*Noticing the maid*) What are you looking for? Is something missing?

MAID: Oh, Your Highness! The pearl necklace has disappeared. I fell asleep and failed to do my duty. Forgive me, I beg you.

PRINCESS: You fell asleep! And someone took my necklace? Who could have done such a deed?

All this time the gardener had been working nearby.
Thus, when he heard the princess cry out, he ran to
her aid.

GARDENER: What has happened, your Highness?

PRINCESS: This foolish girl did not guard my necklace. She has allowed someone to steal my greatest treasure. Whatever will I do?

MAID: Alas! I was careless and fell asleep. Now the pearl necklace has disappeared. I must find it. I beg you to help me.

So the gardener went to the aid of the princess and her maid. They looked on the shore. They looked in the bushes. They even looked in the stream. But not once did they look in the hollow of the tree.

GARDENER: I fear the necklace has been stolen, your Highness. But we are the only ones to have entered the garden. Perhaps a monkey came down from the treetops to do this terrible deed.

PRINCESS: Of course! How wise you are! We must watch the monkeys and see which one has stolen my pearl necklace.

But finding the necklace was not an easy task. The princess looked into the trees and her heart sank. There were so many monkeys! Meanwhile, the gardener walked back and forth, back and forth, frowning as he did so. Finally, he stopped and smiled.

GARDENER: I have just thought of an idea! Go back to the palace, your Highness. I promise that your necklace will be returned by morning.

PRINCESS: Your task is not simple. But if you do as you promise, your reward will be a sack of gold coins.

GARDENER: I do not need a reward, your Highness. Not even a sack of gold coins. It is my duty to help you. Never fear. I will return your greatest treasure.

So the princess and her maid returned to the palace, and the gardener rushed away to the marketplace. There he bought as many strings of bright-colored glass beads as he could carry. Then he left the marketplace and rushed back to the garden.

That night while the monkeys were asleep, the gardener tossed the strings of beads all around. Then he hid behind a bush and waited for morning to come.

The monkeys woke at sunrise. When they saw the glass beads, they quickly slid down from the trees. Laughing happily, they dressed themselves up in the shining necklaces. All but one—the vain monkey.

High in a treetop, next to the hollow where the treasure was hidden, sat the vain monkey. She smiled a secret smile and paid no attention to the glass beads. Thus, from his hiding place, the gardener paid special attention to her.

Meanwhile, the monkeys began fighting with one another.

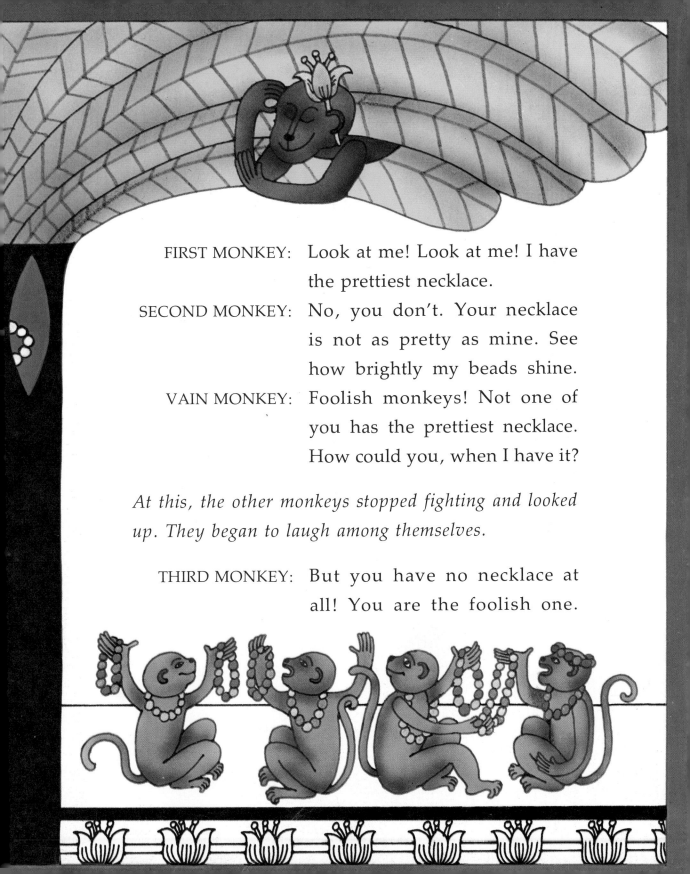

FIRST MONKEY: Look at me! Look at me! I have the prettiest necklace.

SECOND MONKEY: No, you don't. Your necklace is not as pretty as mine. See how brightly my beads shine.

VAIN MONKEY: Foolish monkeys! Not one of you has the prettiest necklace. How could you, when I have it?

At this, the other monkeys stopped fighting and looked up. They began to laugh among themselves.

THIRD MONKEY: But you have no necklace at all! You are the foolish one.

The vain monkey grew angry. She reached into the hollow of the tree where the pearl necklace glowed like a string of tiny moons. She took the necklace out and put it around her neck. Then she slid down from the tree and proudly danced along the garden path. She came closer and closer to the place where the gardener was hiding. Quick as a flash, he jumped out and grabbed her with his strong hands.

GARDENER: Aha! I've caught you. Now give me the pearl necklace.

The vain monkey was too surprised to run away. Thus, the gardener was able to get the necklace and rush to the palace where the princess and her maid were waiting.

PRINCESS: You found my necklace! How clever and wise you are! Now I will give you the reward. Take this sack of gold coins to spend as you wish.

And so the gardener took the gold coins and spent them wisely. As for the vain monkey, it would be nice to say that she never stole anything again. But I wonder if that is true.

The storyteller seems unwilling to believe that the vain monkey never stole anything again. Why?

How the Rhinoceros Lost His Smooth Skin

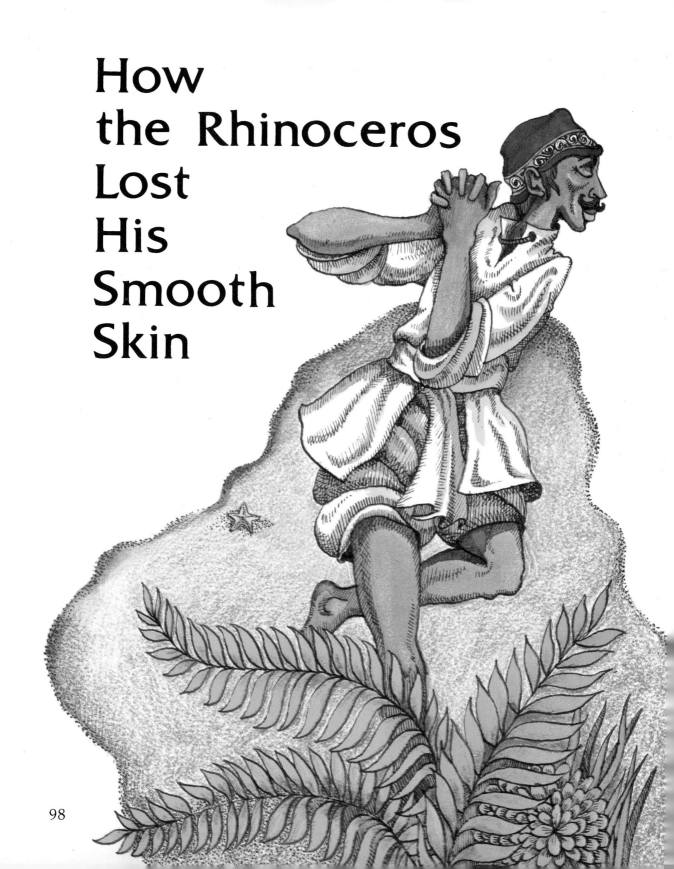

Once upon a time, on an island in the Red Sea, there lived a Parsee. He lived alone with nothing but a hat, a knife, and a cooking oven.

One day the Parsee took some flour, and water, and cherries, and sugar, and mixed himself a cake. Now he didn't mix just a plain cake. No, indeed! The Parsee used a whole sack of cherries and a whole pound of sugar. Thus, the cake was two feet across and three feet thick. The Parsee put the cake in the oven and baked it until it was all brown and smelled delicious.

Just as the Parsee was about to eat the cake, there came walking down to the beach an ugly rhinoceros. In those days the rhinoceros had smooth skin which fit him quite tight. There were no folds to be seen in it. He had huge jaws, a great horn on his nose, and very poor manners. He had no manners then, he has no manners now, and he never will have any manners.

The rhinoceros said, "How!" and frightened the Parsee. When the Parsee saw the ugly rhinoceros, he climbed up the trunk of the nearest tree, leaving the cake behind.

The rhinoceros upset the oven with his nose, and the cake rolled in the sand. He lifted the cake with the tip of his horn, and it disappeared inside his huge jaws. Then he went away, waving his tail as he walked up the beach.

Soon afterwards the Parsee slid down the tree trunk and put the oven on its legs. Then he stamped one foot and sang this song:

"Them that takes cakes
Which the Parsee-man bakes
Makes awful mistakes!"

And there was more meaning to this song than one might think.

Five weeks later, there was a terrible heat wave. The Parsee shed his hat, and the ugly rhinoceros shed his skin. Now in those days the skin of the rhinoceros was buttoned with three buttons and looked like a raincoat. To escape the heat, the rhinoceros went to the beach, carrying his skin over his shoulder. He went straight into the water, leaving his skin lying on the shore.

In a little while the Parsee just happened by and found the skin. He smiled a smile that ran around his face at least two times. He clapped his hands together and danced around the skin. Then he stamped one foot and sang his song again:

"Them that takes cakes
Which the Parsee-man bakes
Makes awful mistakes!"

The Parsee hurried to his camp and filled his hat with cake crumbs. Then he took that skin, and he shook that skin, and he rubbed that skin just as full of scratchy cake crumbs as it could possibly hold. When he had finished, he climbed a nearby tree trunk and waited for the rhinoceros to come out of the water and put on his skin.

And the rhinoceros did. He buttoned the three buttons, and the skin tickled him like cake crumbs in bed. He tried to scratch but that made things worse. He lay down in the sand and rolled and rolled and rolled. Every time he rolled, the cake crumbs tickled him worse and worse and worse.

104

Finally, the ugly rhinoceros ran to the tree and rubbed and rubbed and rubbed himself against it. He rubbed so much and so hard that he rubbed his skin into a great fold over his shoulder. And he rubbed another great fold on the underside of his body where the buttons used to be—but he had rubbed them all off. And he rubbed some more folds over his legs. And he grew angry, but that didn't bother the crumbs in the least. They were inside his skin and they tickled.

At last the rhinoceros went away, very cross indeed, and scratchy, too. From that day to this, every rhinoceros has great folds in his skin, all on account of the cake crumbs that tickled inside.

All this time the Parsee had been hiding in the tree, clapping his hands together.

Now he slid down the trunk and went along home. There he took some flour, and water, and cherries, and sugar, and mixed another cake two feet across and three feet thick. And this one he ate himself.

Can You Guess?

1. How is a watch like a river?

 2. Why are fish so smart?

3. Why do Granny's slippers last so long?

 4. Why does time fly so fast?

5. How is the letter **e** like an island?

Answers

5. It's right in the middle of the sea.
4. People are always trying to kill it.
3. She never wears them out.
2. They swim in schools.
1. It won't run very long without winding.

106

Mixed Feelings

Roper

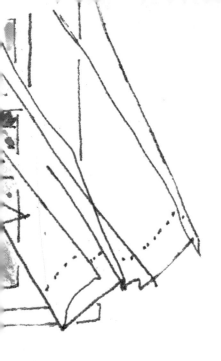

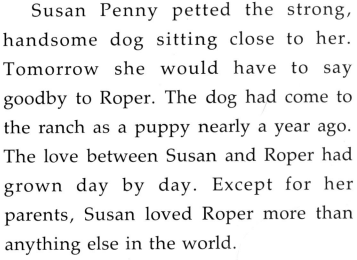

Susan Penny petted the strong, handsome dog sitting close to her. Tomorrow she would have to say goodby to Roper. The dog had come to the ranch as a puppy nearly a year ago. The love between Susan and Roper had grown day by day. Except for her parents, Susan loved Roper more than anything else in the world.

Susan hated the thought of taking Roper back to the training school! Yet she could still recall what the man had told her the day she and her parents had picked up the puppy. "Remember," he said, "you'll have to give Roper up some day so that he can be trained to serve a blind person."

"Well," thought Susan to herself, "we can still spend today together."

"Come with me, Roper," she said, jumping up from the chair. "Let's go outside for a while."

Roper followed Susan outdoors. The dog dashed across the grass, barking joyfully. He had almost reached the north end of the ranch when Susan caught up with him. Just then a truck roared past on the highway. Roper had seen it coming, but he jumped and turned away. His ears flattened against his head, and he cried softly.

"What's the matter, Roper?" asked Susan with a frown. "You ought to be used to traffic by now." She bent down and gave him a hug. "Come on, Boy. Let's go home."

Susan felt better as she walked toward the house. The way the truck had frightened the dog somehow gave her hope. "But hope for what?" she asked herself.

After dinner, Susan sat at the desk in her room and began a report for the training school. She hadn't written very much when her father stopped at the doorway.

"How are you coming?" asked Mr. Penny.

"OK. Roper's a good dog, except . . ." Susan stopped in the middle of the sentence.

"Except what?" questioned her father.

"We were out at the north end of the ranch today," said Susan as she put down her pencil. "A truck came along, and Roper acted as if he were afraid."

Mr. Penny came in and sat on the bed. "Roper's fear of traffic could cause problems," he said. "Have you written that in your report?"

Susan got up from the desk and sat next to her father. "I hate to report every little thing."

"Anything important ought to be reported," replied Mr. Penny. "Remember, Roper will help the blind, and he must be able to handle lots of problems. That's why he'll be given so many tests at the training center."

"Do you think I'll get Roper back if he fails any of the tests?" asked Susan.

"I wouldn't count on it," answered her father. "The love and training he receives will prepare him to be the eyes for a blind person."

Susan knew what her father meant. It wasn't right to want Roper to fail any of the tests, but still . . .

That night Susan hardly slept. She must decide what to report. Was Roper a dog a blind person could depend on? Roper was strong and smart, but he must be more than that. He must be able to help his master handle many different problems.

Put to the Test

Susan was at her desk early the next morning. She had the report written before her parents were awake.

Shortly after breakfast, she and her father took Roper to the training school. Mr. Drew, one of the trainers, met them as they arrived at the gate. "That's a fine-looking dog," he said.

"Thank you," said Susan. "Here's my report."

Mr. Drew quickly looked it over. "Afraid?" he asked as he read a sentence on the last page. "Are you certain there's no mistake?"

"The traffic in town never seemed to bother Roper," answered Susan. "But yesterday we were out walking, and he jumped as a truck went by. He acted as if he were afraid."

"A jumpy guide dog could prove hard to handle," replied Mr. Drew. "In times of trouble, he might think of himself instead of his master."

Mr. Drew finished reading the report. "We'll keep him for a while and see how he does in the training program."

Susan hated to leave Roper behind. To make matters worse, the dog could sense something was wrong and began barking wildly. He tried to follow Susan and her father as they got into the car. Susan swallowed hard and forced back the tears.

"We'll take good care of Roper," Mr. Drew said kindly. "And we'll let you know if he makes the grade."

"What if he doesn't?" asked Susan.

"Then it's possible you'll get him back," answered the trainer.

As Susan and her father drove away they could hear the dog barking. "Don't worry," said Mr. Penny. "Roper will be fine."

At home, Susan felt lost without Roper. She felt worse in her room, which Roper had shared with her. She kept looking at the place beside her bed where he had slept. "I've got to forget him," she told herself with a sigh. Then she lay on the bed and stared at the ceiling.

The last thing she thought of before falling asleep was the training program. She wondered if Roper would make the grade and prove to be a good guide dog.

One Sunday afternoon, several months later, a car drove up to the ranch. It was Mr. Drew. "Roper passed the tests," he said as he came up the walk. "You did a good job."

"Great," replied Susan, trying to smile. "Wasn't Roper afraid of the traffic—even once?"

"I'm glad you brought that to our attention," said the trainer. "Roper was frightened by the sound made by the trucks, not the cars. So we walked him around some trucks every day until he got over his fear. That dog ought to be able to handle anything now."

Mrs. Penny looked at her daughter. "Would you want to raise another puppy?" she asked.

"No," answered Susan, swallowing hard. She hadn't forgotten what it had been like to give Roper up.

"Well, let me know if you change your mind," said Mr. Drew.

The next day Susan was riding home on the school bus. When it stopped for a traffic light, a blind man with a guide dog caught her attention. The dog sat quietly while its master spoke to another man. Then the dog moved forward, guiding the man to the corner. When the light changed and everyone started across the street, it carefully led its blind master to the other side.

Susan was as proud of the dog as if she had trained it herself. She could picture Roper doing just what this dog had done.

That evening Susan told her parents what she had seen. "I'd like another puppy from the training school," she added.

Mr. Penny looked surprised. "Are you sure?" he asked.

Susan smiled broadly. "Yes," she answered. "I'm really sure now."

Team Work

A guide dog and a blind person are able to walk down a crowded sidewalk without bumping into anyone. Together they can cross a busy street in safety. The blind person who has learned to depend on a guide dog can move about with quite a bit of freedom.

A guide dog and a blind person must receive training if they are to work together as a team. To get this training, they both become pupils in a special school.

The dog enters the school first and receives about four months of training. During the first stage the dog is taught to follow simple directions, such as "Come," "Sit," and "Stay." If the dog proves to be a good pupil and is suited to the program, it can begin the next stage.

The dog is taken outside the school grounds for the second stage of training. It is taught to lead the trainer along the sidewalks and across the streets. The dog must learn not to be bothered by other animals or people who pass by. It must also learn to warn its trainer of any possible danger. If the dog passes the tests at the end of this stage, it is ready to begin training in a large city.

During the third stage the dog must learn to handle the problems of hurrying crowds and heavy traffic. Finally it is ready to begin working with the person it will serve.

At this stage the blind person enters the school and will be trained with the dog that best suits his or her needs. During the training program both of them are pupils and must learn to work together. The dog will have the task of guiding the blind person around the city in safety. The blind person will have the task of feeding and caring for the dog.

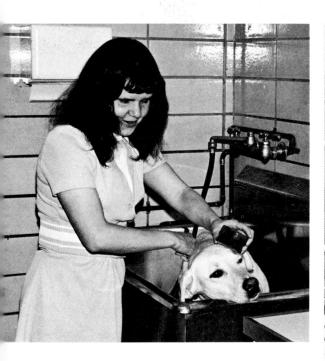

Together they will learn to find certain places—stores, offices, street corners, and bus stops. Together they will learn to move about with the greatest possible freedom. The safety of the blind person will depend on the way they work together. A special kind of feeling grows between the two of them. They will share their lives as a team.

General Takes the Cake 🧁

"Look at Jack's huge dog!" yelled Maria.

"Wow!" shouted Charly. "I thought your dog was a puppy."

"General is a puppy," said Carol, who was Jack's older sister.

"He's only nine months old, and he already weighs fifty pounds," boasted Jack.

"That's almost as much as I weigh," said Maria. "I didn't think a dog that big could come to school."

"I checked with Mr. Peterson yesterday," replied Jack. "He told me I could bring him today."

"But what's he doing here?" asked Charly.

"Today is Kim's birthday, and we're having a party," explained Jack. "I thought it'd be fun to bring my dog. The kids in my class don't know he's coming, and he'll be a big surprise."

"He's big all right," said Maria, laughing.

General leaped up and tried to sniff the children's faces. He barked cheerfully, delighted with the attention he was getting. Suddenly he jumped up and put his paws on Charly's shoulders. "Hey!" shouted Charly. "He likes me."

Jack couldn't help boasting some more. "Of course he does. He's a very friendly dog."

"He's heavy, too," said Charly. "How much did you say he weighs?"

"Around fifty pounds," replied Jack.

Before long the bell rang, and General tried to follow the children as they ran toward the door. He pulled at the leash with all his might.

"Hey, quit that," demanded Carol. "We're going in now, and you'd better be good!"

But General still wanted to play, so Carol was forced to wrap the leash around her hand to keep him from getting loose. "General thinks school is one big playground," she said as they went inside.

When the children reached the classroom door, Jack turned to his sister and said, "Wait here. I'll find out when you can come in."

As he entered the room he saw the teacher near the chalkboard. Kim was in the back of the room unwrapping a tray of strawberry cupcakes.

Jack walked up to Mr. Peterson. "I brought my dog to school," he whispered. "May I show him to the class now?"

"Sure," replied Mr. Peterson. "Where is he?"

"Out in the hall with my sister," answered Jack. "I told her to wait there until you said it was OK to bring him in."

Mr. Peterson thought for a moment. "Tell you what," he said. "Let's sing 'Happy Birthday' to Kim first, and then you can ask your sister to bring in the dog."

After the class sang, their teacher spoke to them. "Today we're going to have a double treat. Kim has brought cupcakes for everyone. But before she passes them out, Jack would like us to meet General."

"General?" wondered Kim. "Who's that?"

Jack walked over and opened the door. The huge puppy shot forward, pulling the leash out of Carol's hand. He charged past Mr. Peterson's desk, barking excitedly as he went. He ran to the chalkboard and sniffed. Chalk dust blew into the air.

Then General saw it—the tray of strawberry cupcakes! Before anyone realized what was happening, he dashed toward Kim's treat.

"Grab him!" screamed Jack.

But it was too late—the tray had been knocked to the floor, and strawberry cupcakes were rolling everywhere! By the time Carol reached him, the dog had already swallowed his third cupcake.

Carol frowned and picked up the leash. "You're a bad dog, General," she said. The puppy just hung his head.

The children were delighted when they saw General's nose all covered with strawberry frosting. Even Mr. Peterson had to laugh.

"I'm sorry, Kim," said Jack as he picked up the tray. "I never thought General would get loose. I'll bring another treat tomorrow to make up for the cupcakes he ate."

"That's OK," she said, trying to smile. "It really wasn't your fault. Besides, watching General eat the cupcakes was more fun than eating them ourselves!"

"I guess our double treat turned into double trouble," said their teacher.

Everyone agreed. And to be sure, General was never again invited to another class party.

The Trouble with Horses

Alfred was so excited he couldn't stand still. A man had given a whole stable of horses to the town so the children could ride. And for the first time Alfred was going to ride a horse!

He hopped from foot to foot as he stood in line waiting for his turn. Then, with one big hop, he landed in front of his friend Joe.

"No, you don't!" said Joe, pulling Alfred back by his shirt.

Alfred climbed up on the fence, locking his feet beneath the bar. "My name begins with an *A* so I should go first," he said.

"In that case," replied Margaret, "I should go first. My real name is Abigail Margaret."

Just then the gate to the ring was opened, and Joe went in first.

131

When Alfred's turn came, he marched into the
ring. All he could see were the legs of horses, and
all he could hear was the pounding of hoofs. Then
he noticed the stable boy, who was holding a
huge, gray horse by the reins.

"Where's my horse?" Alfred wanted to know.

"Right here! His name is Big Judge," answered the stable boy in a voice that showed how lucky Alfred was. "He's as light as a feather and as hoppy as a jumping bean!"

Alfred's face turned pale. "I guess I'll wait for a smaller horse," he replied politely.

"You take 'em as they come," said the stable boy, "or you miss your turn." He looked at Alfred. "You're not scared, are you?"

"I'm not scared," boasted Alfred. "Not at all. I'll get on that old horse." He eyed the great horse, who kept taking little sideways steps, never standing still for a moment.

"Up you go," said the stable boy as he lifted Alfred high in the saddle.

The boy showed Alfred how to hold the reins with one hand and the pommel with the other. Alfred held on as tight as he could, but neither the reins nor the pommel made him feel safe.

"Why doesn't Big Judge stand still?" he wondered.

The horse turned his head and looked back at Alfred with big, glassy eyes. The stare made Alfred feel uneasy.

Then Big Judge sneezed, and water from the horse's nose got all over Alfred's jeans in little drops. Alfred didn't like that at all. Nor did he like the way the horse curled back his lips, showing great white teeth.

Suddenly the horse shook all over, as if he were going to wiggle out of his skin.

Alfred's face grew paler. "Take me off," he begged.

"You just got on," replied the stable boy.

Big Judge danced sideways and sneezed a second time. "Make him stand still," Alfred begged again.

Before the boy could answer, a piece of paper was lifted from the ground and blown into the air. The big horse jumped, barely taking his front feet off the ground. Alfred dropped the reins and grabbed Big Judge's long black hair, holding on with all his might.

"Take me off!" he begged in a frightened voice. "I have to go home now."

"I bet you don't have to go home," said the stable boy as he lifted Alfred out of the saddle. "You're just scared."

Alfred left the ring, his head down and his hands stuffed into the pockets of his jeans. All the way home he kicked the toes of his sneakers into the cracks of the sidewalk.

Later, in his room, Alfred looked at the toy horse sitting on top of his desk. The horse had been a birthday present, and he had named it Sport.

"They shouldn't have given me such a giant horse to ride," he told Sport. The toy horse seemed to look right at Alfred and nod as if it agreed with him.

In the middle of the night Alfred had a terrible dream. He dreamed that Sport had jumped off the desk and turned into a huge, gray horse. It curled back its lips, and Alfred could feel its warm breath on his face.

Alfred woke up, scared and shaking. He lay there in the dark room and faced the truth. He was afraid of horses. It would be his biggest secret because he hated to be afraid.

Now Alfred knew very well that everyone is afraid of something. Abigail Margaret, who lived down the block, acted silly about snakes. Last week when he'd brought a little green garden snake into her house, she'd screamed, "Get it out! Get it out!" She had scared that baby snake a lot more than it had scared her.

His little sister didn't like the way the house seemed to sigh or groan in the middle of the night. If she woke up and heard strange noises, she'd climb in bed with their parents. Why, even Mom was afraid of spiders, and he thought everyone knew that spiders were a sign of good luck.

But Alfred was sure his fear was different. He was sure his friends would make fun of him if they found out, and that would be awful!

Now that there were horses in the park, the neighborhood kids went riding every Saturday. "All anyone ever talks about is horses!" said Alfred as he walked along kicking the cracks in the sidewalk.

He thought up all kinds of excuses not to ride. He sneezed a lot, and he blew his nose noisily. Now, everyone knows that mothers never allow you to ride when you have a cold.

He got his finger caught in the car door, and it really hurt. But the bright side was a big bandage. You can't hold onto the reins very well with a bandage on your finger. And so your friends will never ask you to go riding with them.

The Trouble with Alfred

Finally the Saturday came when Alfred ran out of excuses. He stayed home that day, sitting in his tree house in the backyard, playing alone. Even his sister went to the park. It was lonely trying to keep a secret.

One Wednesday, after many days of no excuses, Alfred slipped and fell out of the oak tree in the side yard. His mother took him straight to the hospital.

"There doesn't seem to be much wrong here," said the doctor. "No bones broken." However, he agreed that a sling might make Alfred's arm feel better.

Alfred forgot to wear the sling until Saturday morning. He was just putting it on when Joe yelled at him from the front porch, "Alfred, are you coming?"

"On my way," Alfred shouted back.

He walked outside. Joe was leaning against the porch railing and noticed the sling. "What happened?" he asked. "How come you got a sling on? Hurt your arm?"

"I fell out of a tree and had to go to the hospital," explained Alfred. "Come on, I'll race you to the corner."

Halfway down the street Abigail Margaret was waiting in her yard. She joined the race, pigtails flying, and won easily.

"Girls are fastest," she said. "I'm not even out of breath."

"That's because you only had to run half as far," Alfred told her.

The children headed toward the park, and this time Alfred went along with them. After all, he had his arm safely in the sling!

"Sorry, kids," said the stable boy as they reached the gate. "The riding class has taken most of the horses on an all-day ride."

Joe looked around. "Hey, Alfred, have you ever been in the stable?"

Alfred shook his head. He didn't feel that he'd missed anything.

"We go almost all the time, don't we, Joe?" boasted Margaret.

"Well, I do," answered Joe. "I don't know about you." He stuck his hand into his jeans pocket and brought out two carrots.

"I always bring stuff along to feed the horses," he explained.

"So do I," said Margaret as she pulled a small green apple from her jacket pocket.

"Come on," yelled Joe. "Let's go feed the horses."

"You heard the stable boy say that most of the horses are gone," said Alfred.

"Old Hunter'll be there," replied Joe. "He's too old to ride anymore. Maybe there'll be some others left."

So Alfred slowly followed behind his friends. When he entered the stable, his eyes took a few seconds to get used to the dark.

Then he noticed a long line of double doors on both sides of the stable. The bottom doors were closed, but the top ones were wide open.

"Hey, watch where you're stepping," warned Margaret.

Just then a huge, gray horse leaned its head out of the open door right above Alfred. Its lips curled back, and its glassy eyes stared down at him. Alfred jumped. He turned pale, and his heart began to pound inside his shirt.

143

"It's Big Judge!" shouted Margaret. "He must like you, Alfred." The horse bent his neck toward the children, shaking his head sideways as he did so.

"He likes my carrots," said Joe, holding out a carrot in his open hand.

As the horse opened his lips Alfred expected to see Joe's hand disappear forever inside the huge jaws. Instead, Big Judge grabbed the carrot lightly with his mouth and began to chew. Carrot juice dripped from his mouth while the big jaws crunched on the carrot.

Then Abigail Margaret held out her apple, and the horse reached for it as carefully as he had the carrot. Alfred watched as the juice dripped from Big Judge's mouth.

"Want to give him a carrot?" Joe asked.

"No, thanks, I'd rather not," said Alfred, shaking his head.

"Why not?" asked Joe.

"Because I don't want to," replied Alfred. "That's why!"

"Aw, come on, feed him," demanded Joe, pushing the carrot at Alfred.

Alfred looked at Joe and Margaret. "I can't! I'm afraid," he whispered. Then he turned away to hide the tears.

"Oh, we know that," said Joe and Margaret together.

Alfred's surprise stopped the tears. "You do? How long have you known?"

"Since that first day," replied Joe.

"Me, too," added Margaret.

"And you don't care?" asked Alfred.

"Why should we?" asked Joe. "It's your problem."

"I know," sniffed Alfred.

Then they all laughed. And suddenly Alfred felt better than he had felt in a long time. He looked up and noticed Big Judge's eyes watching him. The horse sneezed, and drops of water fell on the ground.

"He sneezed to clear his head," explained Joe.

"Why does he shake like that?" asked Alfred.

"Oh, that's just the way he scares off the flies," answered Margaret.

Alfred took a deep breath. He liked the smell of the stable now. He put out a timid hand and touched Big Judge lightly on the neck. The horse's hair felt just like his hairbrush at home. Alfred smiled.

"Do you like horses now?" asked Joe.

Alfred nodded. "Only . . . " He stopped in the middle of the sentence.

"Only what?" asked Joe.

"Only the trouble with horses is that you have to ride 'em," answered Alfred.

Me Myself and I

Isn't it strange
That however I change,
I still keep on being me?

Though my clothes get worn out,
Though my toys are outgrown,
I never grow out of me.

I may lose many things and frequently do.
I never lose me.
Does that happen to you?

Eve Merriam

The Friendly Ghost

Julie had never been away from home before, and her first night in the country was a frightening one. Of course, she knew Aunt Jean and Uncle Harry well, for they had often come to the city to visit her parents. But this was the first time she had been at their farm. She didn't know whether she was going to like making friends with horses, and cattle, and chickens.

Julie wished Aunt Jean had never written the letter asking if she could come for a visit. She wished she could go home. She wished . . . Julie rubbed her eyes. She didn't want to cry. After all, she was in the third grade. But she did feel lonely and strange as she stood in the middle of the room before she got ready for bed.

There was a knock at the door. "May I come in, Julie? I've got something for you." It was Uncle Harry's pleasant voice calling her.

"Ye-es," Julie said, swallowing quickly and trying to smile.

"I figured you might get hungry in the night," said Uncle Harry, "so I brought some apples."

He set a plate with three polished apples on the table by the window. "They're the first of the crop. I just picked them today. Aren't they beautiful?"

"Ye-es," answered Julie.

Uncle Harry looked out the window of the ground-floor bedroom. "I used to have this room when I was a boy," he said. "I always liked it because I could watch the horses and cattle in the pasture. I figured you might like to ride one of the horses while you're here."

Julie clapped her hands together. "I'd like that," she said.

Uncle Harry nodded. "Ned is the easiest to ride, but Daisy is all right if she likes you."

"How will I know if she likes me?" questioned Julie.

"Oh, you'll know because Daisy will come right up and rub her nose against you," he replied.

After Julie's uncle left the room, she began to think that life in the country might not be so lonely after all. She undressed quickly and hung up her clothes.

She had just switched off the light in her room and had climbed into bed when Aunt Jean came in to say good night.

"Summer nights can get pretty cool," said Aunt Jean as she put a blanket on the bed. "Sleep well, dear, and don't be alarmed if you hear strange noises in the night. An old house creaks now and then."

"Why?" asked Julie, holding tight to Aunt Jean's hand. Julie didn't want her to leave.

"The boards in an old house have a way of talking to each other, telling about the things they've seen," explained her aunt.

"Does that mean there are ghosts in this house?" cried Julie.

"Goodness no, child!" replied Aunt Jean. "Whoever put such an idea in your head?"

But long after her aunt had left, Julie lay wide awake in the dark, staring at the ceiling. The breeze, blowing through the open window near the head of her bed, tossed the curtains back and forth. Outside the crickets were singing, but inside everything was quiet—or almost quiet.

Now and then a board in the floor would creak, and another one in the wall would answer. Julie shut her eyes tight, not wanting to see what might be in her room, yet quite sure that something was. She peeked into the dark for a moment, but could see nothing. She ducked under the blanket, wishing morning would come soon.

Then Julie remembered the apples Uncle Harry had put on the table and decided to eat one. She sat up and reached out her hand. As she did so, she heard a noise outside the window.

Suddenly, right in front of her eyes, the curtains moved in the breeze, and a long white shape reached into the room. Julie screamed and ducked under the blanket. Then she slid down to the foot of the bed.

Aunt Jean and Uncle Harry came running down the stairs. They switched on the light and pulled back the blanket. Julie peeked out.

"I just saw a ghost!" Julie whispered in a frightened voice. She had to swallow hard to get the words out.

Aunt Jean leaned close. "There isn't a single ghost in this house," she said.

Uncle Harry laughed. "Well, I guess I know one girl who shouldn't eat apples before she goes to sleep."

"But I d-didn't eat an apple," said Julie, with a lump in her throat. "I was just g-going to."

"That's funny," Uncle Harry said. "I'm sure I put three apples on that plate, and now there are only two."

Aunt Jean stared at the plate, saying, "I certainly polished three apples."

Julie shook her head back and forth. "I know I didn't eat one," she said.

Aunt Jean sat on the edge of the bed. "You can go back upstairs, Harry. I'll stay with Julie until she falls asleep."

Julie slid back under the blanket, and she and her aunt talked for a while.

Suddenly Julie pressed Aunt Jean's hand tightly. "What's that?" whispered the young girl. A lump of fear began to rise in her throat.

"Just a board creaking in the floor," answered Aunt Jean. "You'll get used to hearing sounds like that in this old house."

Although Julie felt better, she didn't close her eyes. Instead, she watched the curtains blowing about in the breeze. She wasn't afraid now. She knew that if the strange white shape reached in through the window again, Aunt Jean would send it away.

But nothing happened—not one single thing. And before long, Julie settled down and was soon fast asleep.

At breakfast, they all laughed about the strange visitor. Even Julie found it easy to joke about ghosts in the daytime. Uncle Harry said she must have had a dream. Aunt Jean agreed. But neither of them could explain why there were only two apples left when there had been three apples on the plate.

Aunt Jean finally said, "I figure you must have eaten an apple in your sleep, dear." But Julie shook her head back and forth. She was sure that she hadn't.

The Ghost Returns

The first day Julie spent in the country was a busy one. For a while she helped Aunt Jean pull weeds in the garden. Afterwards she helped Uncle Harry feed the chickens and pick apples in the orchard.

Later she leaned against the pasture fence and watched the horses. She wondered when she would be allowed to ride one of them. Although she liked Ned, the white horse named Daisy was her favorite.

Julie spent the afternoon picking berries with Aunt Jean. When evening came, the young girl was quite ready to take a bath and go to bed.

"No ghosts tonight," said Aunt Jean as Julie walked out of the bathroom. "If you do hear something, remember that it's just the wind at the window or the old boards creaking in the floor. Only human beings live in this house."

Julie was too tired and too happy to worry about ghosts. She settled down in bed, remembering all the wonderful things she had done.

When a board creaked, she smiled to herself and thought how friendly it was to have a house so old that it could speak. Perhaps if she spent enough time listening, she would be able to tell what it was saying. Then she could talk back, although she was much too sleepy to do that tonight.

And then suddenly she wasn't sleepy anymore. The curtains moved, and the long white shape she had seen the night before came into the room!

Julie didn't waste any time screaming. She ducked under the blanket and wiggled down to the foot of the bed. That shape had to be a ghost. It just couldn't be human! She decided not to take any chances and kept her head covered until morning.

When Aunt Jean came in to wake Julie, she found her hidden beneath the pillows and the blanket.

Julie remembered what had happened. "It was a ghost," she whispered in a weak voice. "I know it was."

Aunt Jean noticed Julie's pale face. "That's impossible," she answered, smiling. "You know there aren't such things as ghosts—not in this house, anyway."

Then she saw the plate on the table and smiled. "Why, Julie, you've eaten another apple! Uncle Harry will be glad that you like them so much. And I notice you even threw away the core."

Julie looked at the table. There was only one apple left on the plate!

There were pancakes for breakfast, and somehow Julie was able to laugh and talk with her aunt and uncle. The mystery of the night before seemed far away.

After breakfast Uncle Harry took Julie out to the meadow. "Which horse would you rather ride?" he asked, rubbing Ned's smooth neck.

Julie didn't waste any time deciding. "I'd like to ride Daisy."

"Daisy doesn't make friends easily, but I'm sure she'll be all right with you." Julie's uncle lifted her onto the horse's broad back. Then he got on Ned, and they rode across the meadow.

Uncle Harry was surprised when he saw how Daisy acted with the young girl. "I guess you've been making up to Daisy," he teased. "Have you been feeding her sugar so she'll like you?"

Julie smiled, glad that her uncle didn't think she was scared of everything.

That night Julie went bravely off to bed. Aunt Jean offered to sleep with her, but Julie refused. She felt quite certain that she had been dreaming. It was impossible to believe that a ghost could live in a house as nice as this one.

There was still a big mystery about the disappearing apples, though. Could she have eaten them in her sleep? But what had happened to the seeds—and the cores?

Aunt Jean smiled as she switched off the light in Julie's room. "Good night, dear, and sleep well," she said. "I hope you won't have any dreams at all tonight."

Julie was so tired and happy that she soon fell into a sound sleep. She would have slept until morning, but she heard a strange sound during the night. Feeling something warm near her face, she opened her eyes.

Moonlight filled the room. In its soft glow, Julie could clearly see that something had pushed its head through the open window. She sat up in bed, and a lump of fear rose in her throat. She opened her mouth to scream.

Then suddenly Julie saw what was there. She put out her hand and touched the smooth white head. "Hello, Daisy," she said softly. "We had a nice ride today, didn't we?"

Daisy tossed her head and made a little sound.

Julie wished she had some sugar to give the horse. She explained to Daisy that she would bring some to the meadow the next morning.

"Do you like apples?" she asked, remembering there was one on the plate. But when she looked, the plate was empty! Not one single apple was left.

A wide smile spread over Julie's face. "I guess you do like apples," she said. "Even the cores."

Daisy drew her head back from the window. Then she kicked up her back feet, easily jumped the low fence, and dashed across the meadow.

Uncle Harry and Aunt Jean could hardly believe what Julie told them the next morning. But when they saw the hoof marks on the grass, they had to agree. Julie's ghost was only a friendly visitor who liked apples as much as she liked the girl from the city.

How to Make Clue Cookies

Would you like to make a delicious treat? This is what you must do.

1. Put 1 cup of light corn syrup into a pan.

2. Mix 1 cup of sugar with the syrup.

3. Heat the mix until it comes to a boil.
   Then add:
   1 cup of peanut butter
   6 cups of corn flakes

4. Spread the mix evenly into a flat, buttered pan.

5. Let the mix cool, and cut it into squares.

Now watch the cookies disappear!

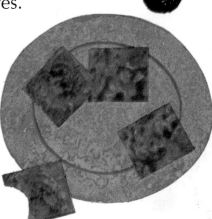

Jimmy Takes Vanishing Lessons

Every morning the school bus picked up Jimmy Holiday near the road that led to the old, empty house. And every afternoon the bus dropped him off in the same place. So twice a day the bus stopped at the mysterious road.

There really wasn't much of a road left anymore. It was covered with weeds and berry bushes. The trees on both sides pressed in so closely that the branches met overhead. The road seemed mysterious even on sunny days.

One day the bus driver had pointed to the road. "People who go there after dark vanish into thin air," she had said. "There's a haunted house just around the curve in the road. The owners put it up for sale years ago, but no one would buy it. You ought to know about that house, Jimmy. It once belonged to your grandfather."

Jimmy's Aunt Pat owned the house now, but she would never talk to him about it. She said the stories he'd heard were silly, and there were no such things as ghosts.

"If the villagers would quit telling tales about the house, I'd put it up for sale again. Or at least try to rent it," his aunt had said. "Then we'd have all the money we need. Why, I might even take you to the movies."

Jimmy had never seen a movie in his whole life. How he wished the house would be rented!

He really didn't believe in ghosts. Yet the house had been rented twice, and each time the people had moved out. They said the things that happened there were just too strange.

Jimmy thought about the house a lot. If only Aunt Pat could rent it! If only he could prove there weren't any ghost! One Saturday while his aunt was gone, he took the key to the haunted house and started down the mysterious road.

"Ghost stories are just tales people make up," he thought. But when he rounded the curve in the road, he wasn't sure. The dusty windows and the shadows gave the house a haunted look.

"Oh, come on!" he told himself. And he lifted his head and bravely marched through the long grass to the porch.

Then Jimmy froze. His feet didn't seem to want to go up the steps. It took him a few minutes to force his feet to move. When at last they did, he marched right up to the front door. He set his teeth hard and put the key in the lock. It turned with a squeak. He pushed the door open and went inside.

Entering the house was the bravest thing that Jimmy had ever done. He found himself in a dark hall filled with shadows. He left the door open so he would be able to see. On his right, a flight of stairs led to the second floor. Except for a table and a chair, the hall was empty.

As he stood there, the hall grew darker. A huge shadow seemed to block out the light from the doorway. Jimmy froze on the spot. His throat felt tight, and his heart pounded faster and faster. He whirled around quickly, but nothing was there.

Jimmy drew a deep breath. "It was just a cloud passing over the sun," he thought. But suddenly the door began to swing slowly back and forth. Before he could reach it, the door slammed shut. And then, as he pulled on the handle to get out, Jimmy saw the ghost!

It behaved as one might expect a ghost to behave—a tall white figure gliding silently down the stairs. Jimmy gave a yell, slammed the door behind him, and shot down the front steps.

How to Deal with a Ghost

Jimmy didn't stop running until he was well around the curve in the road. Then, weak with fear, he sat down on a log to catch his breath.

"Wow!" he said. "I've seen a ghost! It was as white as chalk. That was awful!"

After a few minutes Jimmy settled down. "What was so awful?" he wondered to himself. "The ghost was only trying to scare me, gliding down the stairs like that. Pretty silly way for a ghost to behave."

Jimmy always got mad when someone tried to scare him. Now he was really mad! He jumped off the log and started back. "I'm going to get that key!" he said to himself.

As he tiptoed up the steps, he saw the door swinging back and forth. When he reached for the key, he heard a tiny squeak. He peeked around the door, and there was the ghost!

It was going back upstairs. But instead of gliding, it was sort of dancing. And with every other step the ghost doubled up laughing. It was enjoying the joke it had just played.

Now Jimmy was madder than ever. He stuck his head around the door and yelled, "Boo!" The ghost let out a scream and whirled two feet into the air.

At that moment Jimmy realized he could scare the ghost even worse than the ghost could scare him. He wasn't afraid anymore, so he walked right into the hall.

The ghost was hanging onto the railing, trying to catch its breath. "Oh, my goodness!" it said. "You scared me!"

"I did, did I?" replied Jimmy. "Now we're even."

"Nothing of the sort," said the ghost. "You aren't very bright. Don't you know that ghosts are supposed to scare people? People aren't supposed to scare ghosts!" It glided down and sat on the bottom step. "Now look here. This would cause me great hardship if human beings should find out they can scare a ghost."

"You mean you don't want me to tell anybody?"

"Suppose we make a deal," said the ghost. "You keep still about scaring me, and I'll teach you how to vanish."

"Sounds like a neat idea!" cried Jimmy. "But—can you vanish?"

"Sure," answered the ghost. And it did. All at once it was gone. Only Jimmy remained in the hall.

But the voice of the ghost continued. "It's pretty neat to be able to disappear. Don't you agree? You could get into the movies free. And your aunt wouldn't be able to find you if she wanted you to help her do something."

"I don't mind helping Aunt Pat," said Jimmy. "And I wish you'd please appear again. I feel funny talking to someone who isn't here."

"Sorry, I forgot," said the ghost, and there it was again, sitting on the bottom step.

"If you don't like vanishing, I could teach you to hang from the lights or glide through a keyhole," said the ghost. It floated over to the door and went right through the keyhole. Then it came back the same way.

"Which trick suits you best?" asked the ghost.

"None of them suit me," answered Jimmy. "There's only one thing you can do to make me promise not to tell. Quit hanging around here. Go live somewhere else. Try the North house up the road. Nobody lives there anymore."

"No, thanks!" shouted the ghost. "During a storm the windows bang, the doors slam, and water drips through the ceiling. Peace and quiet, that's all a ghost wants. Just peace and quiet."

"Well, I don't think you're being fair," said Jimmy. "My aunt can't rent this house on account of you."

"I'm not stopping her from renting it," shouted the ghost. "You can't blame me if people get scared and leave."

"I certainly can!" answered Jimmy. "I'm not making any deals with you, either. I'm going to tell everybody how I scared you."

"Oh, don't tell!" begged the ghost, stamping its foot. "If the news got out, every ghost in the country would be in terrible trouble. What a hardship that would be!"

Jimmy just stood and stared.

"This is my home," cried the ghost. "Thirty years I've lived here. Thirty long years! And you want to throw me out into the cold world. How cruel!" It cried and cried.

Jimmy didn't feel cruel at all. The ghost had driven plenty of other people out into the cold world.

But he didn't think it would do much good to tell people that he had scared a ghost. None of his friends would believe him, and it would be impossible to prove his story. So after a minute he said, "OK, let's make a deal. You teach me to vanish, and I won't tell."

Getting Even

Jimmy didn't say a word to his aunt about the deal he'd made. But every Saturday he went to the haunted house for his vanishing lesson. It was really quite easy, and in a week or two Jimmy caught on. In six weeks the ghost gave him a test, and he got a B. That was a very good grade for a human being. Jimmy thanked the ghost and shook hands with it. "Well, good-by now," he said. "You'll be hearing from me."

"What do you mean by that?" asked the ghost. But Jimmy just laughed and ran off.

That night at supper Aunt Pat asked, "What have you been doing today?"

"I've been learning to vanish," replied Jimmy, putting down his fork.

His aunt looked at him out of the corner of her eye.

"Honest!" said Jimmy. "The ghost up at Grandfather's house taught me."

"Quit telling tales," she demanded. "And will you please—why, where are you?"

"Here, Aunt Pat," he said as he reappeared.

"Goodness me!" she cried, rubbing her eyes.

Jimmy had to disappear twice more before she would believe that he could vanish. She was pretty upset when he explained what he had been doing the past Saturdays. Then he told her about his idea to get rid of the ghost, and she agreed to help him with the plan.

So the next day Aunt Pat went to the old house and started to work. She opened the windows and slammed the doors, hoping the noise would bother the ghost. Soon it came floating into the room. She let out a yell and threw the broom at it. The broom went right through the ghost. It came nearer, waving its arms and groaning, trying to scare her.

Suddenly Jimmy appeared and jumped at the ghost. "Boo!" he screamed. The ghost whirled around, scared silly.

When Aunt Pat saw how scared the ghost was, she wasn't frightened anymore. In fact, she even tried to help it into a chair. Of course, she couldn't help much because her hands went right through it.

"You broke your word!" howled the ghost. "What about our deal? You promised . . . "

"I promised not to tell about scaring you," said the boy, "but I didn't promise not to scare you again."

Then his aunt said, "You really are a ghost! I thought ghost stories were just tales people made up. Well, excuse me, but I really must get on with my work." And she began banging her broom around louder than ever.

The ghost stamped its foot and said, "Honestly! Why do human beings make so much noise? Couldn't you work more quietly?"

"Whose house is this?" demanded Aunt Pat. "If you don't like the noise, move out!"

The ghost sneezed several times from all the dust. "Excuse me," it said. "By the way, where's that boy?" For Jimmy had vanished.

"I'm sure I don't know," she replied. "He might be getting ready to scare you again."

"You ought to make him behave," said the ghost as it sneezed again. "If he were my boy, I'd take a hairbrush to him."

"You might try if you wish," said Aunt Pat. "That is, if you can find him."

She reached right through the ghost and pulled a pillow out from under it. As the ghost glided over to another chair, she added, "Jimmy and I are going to sleep here from now on. You won't get rid of us by playing tricks." With that, the ghost groaned and vanished from sight.

That night Aunt Pat put cotton in her ears and slept with a light on. The ghost howled for a while down in the cellar. Nothing happened, so it came upstairs to scare her. But first it wanted to be sure where Jimmy was. Although the ghost hunted all over, it couldn't find the boy. It kept expecting Jimmy to leap out from some dark corner and scare it into fits. Finally the ghost got so jumpy that it went back to the cellar and hid there for the rest of the night.

The following days were just as bad. Several times the ghost left the cellar, planning to scare Jimmy's aunt while she worked. But she didn't scare at all.

Twice Jimmy was able to appear suddenly and let out a loud yell, scaring the ghost terribly. Soon it began to feel quite tired.

Peace and Quiet

When the house was in apple-pie order, Jimmy and his aunt went to see Mr. and Mrs. Spellman. They were living in a hotel because they couldn't find a house for sale. Aunt Pat hoped they would consider renting her house. But Mr. Spellman said, "No, thank you. We'd rather stay at the hotel. We've heard that your house is haunted! I'll bet you wouldn't dare spend a night there."

"But I have!" she said. "Jimmy and I spent a whole week there."

The Spellmans still refused. "The hotel may not be as roomy as a house," they said, "but at least it's not haunted."

"I'll keep you company if you're scared," offered Jimmy. That made the Spellmans feel foolish, so they changed their mind.

The next day they left the hotel and moved into the house. Jimmy stayed with them for a week, but none of them saw the ghost.

Then one day Jimmy heard that a ghost had been seen at the North farm. He wondered if this was the same ghost that had lived in Aunt Pat's house. Was she finally rid of it after thirty years?

A day or two later Jimmy decided to visit the ghost. As he entered the house he heard howling and groaning upstairs. After a minute the ghost came gliding down the steps.

"Oh, it's you," it said. "Can't you leave me in peace?"

"I just wondered how you're getting along," replied Jimmy.

"Getting along fine," answered the ghost. "This isn't such a bad place after all. Peaceful. Quiet. Nobody playing silly tricks."

"Well," said Jimmy, "I promise not to bother you if you won't bother the Spellmans. But if you go back there . . . "

"Don't worry," said the ghost.

Twice a week Jimmy visited the ghost, and they got to be very good friends. The ghost often came to Jimmy's house for dinner, though, of course, it couldn't eat much. And after dinner it enjoyed watching the movies on TV. The ghost was really a pretty good fellow. Even Aunt Pat liked to have it around.

When the weather grew cold, she began to worry about the ghost. She knew there was no heat at the North place, and the doors and windows were loose. The ghost tried to explain that the cold weather was no bother at all. "That's one good thing about being a ghost," it said.

"Maybe so," she replied, "but just the same, you might freeze."

The next time she invited the ghost to dinner, she gave it a pair of socks she had made. The ghost was so pleased that it broke down and cried. And that made Jimmy's aunt so happy, she broke down and cried, too.

Jimmy didn't cry, but he said, "Wouldn't it be nice if the ghost stayed with us until the cold weather was over?"

"I'd feel much better if it did," answered Aunt Pat. "Then I wouldn't worry about it freezing in that old house."

So the ghost lived with them that winter. And when the weather turned warm, it just stayed on. Jimmy's house must have been a peaceful place. For all anyone knows, the ghost is still there.

The Deserted House

I am afraid—
For I am alone
In the deserted house
That stands tumbledown
In the wood
Everywhere is silent
So silent
You can hear
the silence hanging in the dark air
What was that
That noise! an owl?
I steal outside
To see if anyone is there
No! the wood is still
But the trees seem
To crowd closer
I tremble
I run back inside
Like a streak of lightning,
but inside is even more frightening
Than the wood outside
it's not exciting any more
I'm scared
My heart pulses and
Beats fast

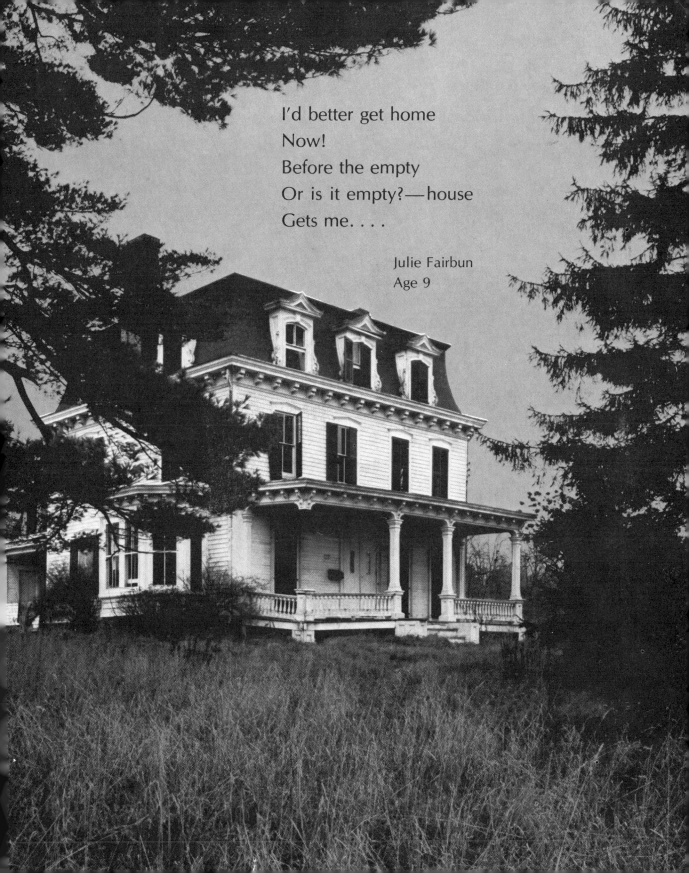

I'd better get home
Now!
Before the empty
Or is it empty?—house
Gets me. . . .

Julie Fairbun
Age 9

The Case of the Missing Camera

Teddy Singer crawled slowly into the Sandy Brooks Detective Office. Sandy was not the least bit surprised to see him with his nose so close to the ground. In fact, Teddy spent most of his time crawling around on his hands and knees.

His hobby was the study of insects. Nobody in East Valley knew more about bees and crickets than he did.

Sandy watched as Teddy stared through a large magnifying glass.

"What do you see?" she asked. "Looks like a plain old caterpillar to me."

"Wrong," whispered Teddy, inching forward to get a closer look. "There's no such thing as a plain old caterpillar. There are at least a thousand different kinds."

"A thousand kinds!" repeated Sandy. "Boy, you sure know a lot about insects."

However, the study of insects wasn't her idea of an interesting hobby. She would much rather solve mysteries.

Teddy finally stood up and put the magnifying glass in his pocket. "Hey, Sandy! I'm sure glad that caterpillar led me in here. I want you to help me solve a mystery."

"No case is too small," boasted Sandy, hoping Teddy wouldn't take her at her word. He might want her to solve the mystery of a vanishing bee!

"What's your problem?" she asked.

"Somebody stole my camera," replied Teddy. "I think it was a ghost."

Sandy swallowed hard. "A g-ghost!" she repeated. "Where?"

"In the old, deserted Price house," he answered.

Sandy shook her head back and forth. "I don't believe in ghosts," she said. "I believe in facts."

"OK," said Teddy. "Here are the facts. This morning I went to the Price house to hunt for interesting insects. I was about to take a picture of a spider when a ghost came floating down the stairs. I thought I'd die!"

"So you got scared and ran out of the house, leaving your camera behind," added Sandy.

"Right," replied Teddy. "But an hour later I went back, and my camera had disappeared."

"Did you notice anything special about the ghost?" asked Sandy.

"It was white," he answered. "And it made a howling noise and whistled a mysterious tune."

"This sounds like a rough case to solve," said Sandy. "Let's not waste any more time talking. We'll go to the Price house and look around."

They jumped on their bikes and started off for the deserted house. On the way they passed the home of Bugs Decker, one of the roughest kids in East Valley. Bugs was a member of the Tigers—a group of boys who seemed to have a hobby of causing trouble.

Two blocks farther on was the old Price place. The big house had not been lived in for thirty years, and no other house in the neighborhood was in worse condition. Broken windows, torn screens, and loose boards made the deserted building look as though it were ready to fall down.

Sandy and Teddy leaned their bikes against an oak tree. They walked through tall grass and weeds and onto the creaky front porch.

Teddy opened the screen door and peeked inside. "Come on," he said. "Follow me."

As the children crept into the hall, Teddy whispered, "I left my camera at the foot of the stairs. When I came back for it, there was the ghost. It was white as a sheet and whistling that mysterious tune. Boy, I almost died of fright!"

Teddy crept the length of the hall and looked into the kitchen. Sandy followed.

"I wanted to take a picture of that!" he said, pointing toward the back door.

Sandy caught her breath. Across the lower half of the screen door was a wheel-shaped web.

"Look at that spider web," said Teddy, his eyes glowing with delight. "I've never seen one in better condition!"

While Teddy was studying the web, Sandy searched the length of the hallway. Suddenly she discovered footprints in the heavy dust on the stairs.

"A ghost does not wear shoes," she thought out loud. "At least not in the summer."

"What was that?" asked Teddy. "Have you found a clue?"

"Footprints," answered Sandy as Teddy hurried in from the kitchen. "Your ghost left some footprints. But it really wasn't a ghost at all. I think I know who scared you."

"You'll be the smartest detective in the whole world if you can solve this mystery!" cried Teddy. "Who do you think made those footprints?"

"Someone who saw you come into the deserted house this morning," replied Sandy. "None other than Bugs Decker."

"How do you figure that?" asked Teddy. "You can't blame Bugs just because he's a member of the Tigers. Lots of people could have seen me come into this house. Why do you think Bugs stole my camera?"

"Because he lives in this neighborhood, and everybody knows what a rough kid he is," answered Sandy. "And because he had his two front teeth knocked out last week fighting with another member of the Tigers."

"What have two missing teeth got to do with this case?" asked Teddy.

"Whenever Bugs tries to talk, he sounds as if he's whistling," explained Sandy.

"Boy, am I a fool!" groaned Teddy. "He must have been wrapped in a sheet. Well, Bugs won't be whistling any more tunes when I . . . "

"Take it easy," said Sandy. "We can't prove anything yet. I want to hear what Bugs has to say for himself."

So Sandy and Teddy left the deserted house and headed for the Deckers. When they arrived, Bugs was sitting in the shade of a tree, eating a sandwich.

"You dressed up in a sheet and scared me in the old Price house," said Teddy.

"Then you stole his camera," added Sandy. "I'll bet a lot of people saw you go up the porch steps."

"Sure," said Bugs, staring at the partly eaten sandwich. "Sure, I saw you go inside, Teddy. Then another kid, carrying a sheet, went in behind you. Pretty soon you came running out, so I went inside to look around. That's when I found this other kid with your camera. As soon as he spotted me, he flew out the back door and into the woods."

"That's a good story," said Sandy. "Good enough to prove you aren't telling the truth."

How did Sandy know that Bugs wasn't telling the truth?

Bugs made up the story about the other boy. If someone had run out the screen door, the spider web would have been broken. But the web was still there!

204

Garden
in the Snow

Luther patted a handful of snow onto the big snowman in the schoolyard. "Spring's late this year," he said to his younger brother, Alfie. "It's April, and there's still snow on the ground."

Alfie nodded. "Our friend here ought to bundle up," he said. He took the scarf from his neck and tied it around the snowman's head. "There! That scarf is even better than a hat."

"A hat!" cried Luther. "I forgot. The spring festival is tonight, and Mother planned to go to Market Square for a new hat. I'm supposed to be taking care of the baby. I'd better get home!"

Luther left his brother and hurried along the path through the woods. He kept his eyes on the ground, watching for a sign of spring, but there was nothing. All that could be seen was a white blanket of snow.

It was a freezing day in April, and Luther was glad his mother had told him to bundle up. He tied the scarf so that it covered his face. Although he was wearing gloves, his fingers felt stiff from the cold. Stuffing his hands deeper into his pockets, he stepped off the path. "Better take the short way home," he decided.

Luther circled around a tall tree. All at once he stopped and stared at the ground ahead. Right in the middle of the snow was a patch of green covered with grass and thick bushes. "It's like a garden in winter!" he cried. "But why has the snow melted only in this spot?"

In the middle of the green patch was a small spring, its water bubbling over several stones. "This must be one of those warm springs I've heard about," he thought to himself. Pulling off his glove, he dipped his finger into the water. It was warm!

"The warm water heats the ground and melts the snow," reasoned Luther. "That's why the grass and the bushes can stay green all through the winter."

He stooped to look more closely at the plant life. Here and there, hidden among the shiny grasses, were some clumps of golden buttercups.

Luther sat down on a nearby log and listened to the bubbling water. How wonderful that plants could be so green and alive when everything else was frozen and looked dead!

Luther had loved the outdoors and growing things ever since he could remember, but never had he felt so excited. He didn't know how long he had sat there when he suddenly noticed the shadows of the trees on the snow. He'd been so interested in the "garden" that he'd forgotten how late he was!

Jumping to his feet, Luther ran through the woods toward home. His mother was waiting at the front door.

"Where were you?" she asked. "I've been worried!"

"I-I stopped in the woods," he explained, pulling off his scarf and gloves. "I discovered the most wonderful thing. A place where the snow has melted and green things grow!"

"I was depending on you to come right home and take care of the baby," said his mother. "Now it's much too late to go to Market Square. Honestly, Luther! Fooling around with seeds and going off into the woods is a waste of time. What will become of you?"

Luther sighed as he warmed himself by the fire. If only his mother could understand how much he loved to study growing things. After all, that was his hobby!

He caught sight of the straw hat hanging from a hook on the kitchen wall. The flowers around the hatband were no longer stiff, the way they had been when his mother had bought the hat.

Suddenly Luther had an idea. Before his mother could say a word, he grabbed his coat and rushed out the door toward the woods.

In a few minutes he reached the patch of green. One by one he picked the golden buttercups and dipped them into the bubbling water. Then he hurried home.

As he opened the door Luther could see his mother standing near the sink. She looked over her shoulder and asked, "Now where did you go?" She sounded angry.

"B-back to the spring," he answered, his lips barely moving. His mother just shook her head.

Luther grabbed the straw hat from the hook and set it on the table. While her back was still turned, he pulled off the old flowers and arranged the fresh blossoms in the hatband.

"Look, Mom," he cried, holding up the hat.

She turned from the sink. Her eyes widened in surprise.

"My hat! Why, it looks lovely. But where—?"

Luther smiled. "The flowers are from my garden. The one I told you about. Do you like the way they're arranged?"

"Indeed I do," she replied. "And I'll be the only lady at the festival wearing a hat with fresh blossoms."

She put the hat on her head and looked in the mirror. "My goodness!" she said, her eyes glowing with happiness. "This fooling around with seeds and going off into the woods—well, maybe it's not such a waste of time after all."

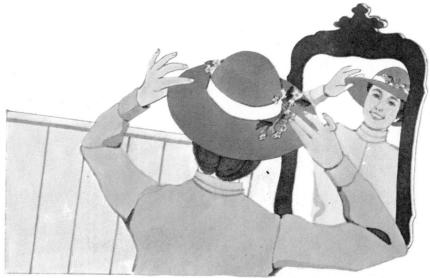

This Wonderful World

It's a wonderful world
With its mountains and plains,
Its cities and towns,
Its automobiles
And aeroplanes,
Its rivers and oceans,
Its forests and trees,
Houses and churches
And factories.
Here are fishes and flowers
And flocks and herds,
Men and women
And children and birds.

Mary Britton Miller

213

Raccoons Are for Wild

"What makes you think a raccoon likes syrup?" asked Jim. "My dog wouldn't touch it. He hates sweet stuff."

"A book I got from the library says a raccoon will eat almost anything," explained Marsha, licking her sticky fingers.

She had gone to great lengths to learn about raccoons and had read every library book she could find about them. More than anything else in the world, Marsha wanted a raccoon. She'd even saved her money to buy a small trap—one that wouldn't harm any animal.

Tonight she and Jim were setting up the trap in a woodsy place near the creek. Inside the trap was a piece of meat Marsha had dipped in syrup.

"That's all we can do now," she said. "We'll check first thing in the morning to see if we've caught a raccoon."

She hardly slept that night, thinking about the raccoon. It would be small and easy to train. It would sleep beside her bed and sit on her lap while she read. It would even go fishing with her! Raccoons love to fish.

The next day Marsha was up before sunrise. Jim came out as soon as she rapped on his window, and the two children hurried to the creek. They could barely see something nibbling at the bait inside the trap. "We got one!" whispered Marsha.

"Its tail looks funny," said Jim. "There aren't any stripes on it. In fact, there's no hair, either!"

"Maybe it's been in a fight," replied Marsha.

Jim shined the flashlight into a pair of black, beady eyes. The nose was long and pointed, but there was no black mask across the face.

"That's not a raccoon!" said Marsha. "Or else it's taken its mask off."

"It's a muskrat!" said Jim. "We'll have to let it go. Or do you want a muskrat for a pet?"

"No," said Marsha. "A muskrat is sort of nice, but a raccoon would be better." So they let the muskrat go free.

The following night the children put apples and corn in the trap. Although they didn't catch anything, they were sure something had nibbled at the bait.

"Look at those footprints," said Marsha. "They must have been made by a raccoon."

The third night the children baited the trap with raw vegetables they had dipped in syrup. Marsha laughed. "Maybe the raccoon will get stuck in the syrup when it goes after the vegetables."

But early the next morning Marsha and Jim found the very same muskrat. It was angrily rapping its tail against the side of the cage, wanting to be set free.

"Let's try another place," sighed Marsha.

"Good idea," agreed Jim. "We can haul the trap to the park and see what happens."

Whispering and tiptoeing, the children again baited the trap and set it under a tree near the birdbath.

But catching a raccoon was not an easy task. That night they caught a rabbit. And the next night they caught another rabbit!

They got into trouble with a policeman, too. "You can't trap animals in the park," he said.

So the children hauled the trap away. Tired and disappointed, they left it on Marsha's back porch.

The next morning Marsha looked out the window and saw something furry in the trap. She rushed outside, hoping to see a striped tail.

But the animal inside the trap barked. It had neither a striped tail nor a mask across its eyes. It was the puppy who lived next door.

"Oh, Curly," cried Marsha. "I'm sorry." She carefully opened the trap door and Curly jumped out. Free at last, the puppy ran home.

The children were disappointed again, but they refused to give up. They continued to bait the trap every day. Meanwhile, Marsha's mother kept talking about the price of meat. And Jim's mother wondered why her fresh vegetables were disappearing so fast.

When Curly was caught a second time, Jim said, "Well, I guess it's back to the muskrats. At least that's better than trapping puppies." So the trap was hauled back to the creek and set down near a hollow log.

The next morning Marsha was awake before daylight. She bounced out of bed, hurried over to Jim's house, and rapped on the window. "Come on, Jim," she called, her voice bubbling with happiness. "I think we got a raccoon."

"OK," he answered, "I'm coming."

The children soon reached the creek. They crept silently toward the trap. "Look!" cried Marsha, grabbing Jim's arm.

A long, striped tail poked through the trap. With the aid of a flashlight the children could see a furry, black mask.

"We did it!" shouted Marsha. "We got our raccoon."

"What a big one!" remarked Jim as he watched the animal nibbling at the bait. "I bet it weighs a lot."

As the children hauled the trap home, they had to be careful that the raccoon didn't scratch them with its sharp claws. "Good thing I read all those library books," boasted Marsha. "That's how I learned you should wear gloves when you handle a wild animal."

The angry raccoon began to hiss and spit. "I don't think it will make a very good pet," remarked Marsha.

"Give it a chance," said Jim. "When it gets used to us, it'll stop hissing and spitting."

"I don't think so," replied Marsha.

Later, when the trap was opened, the raccoon climbed straight up the brick wall outside Marsha's house. There it hung in the corner of the roof, with its face turned to the wall.

When night came, the raccoon slid back down the wall and ran off toward the woods, hissing and spitting all the way.

"Well," remarked Jim, "at least it will be glad to get back with its family."

"I'm sort of glad to see it go," said Marsha. "Those claws were awfully sharp!"

The next morning the children found another raccoon nibbling the bait in the trap. It was the same size as the first one, but it didn't spit or hiss. It just sat in the corner of the trap and stared at them with frightened eyes. Jim gave it some water to dip its food in, but he didn't touch the animal for fear it would bite.

That afternoon Marsha said to Jim, "I remember what you said about the other raccoon—the mean one. I guess its family would be glad to get it back. Do you suppose this raccoon might have a family, too?"

"This is a female raccoon," said Jim. "She might have some babies down by the creek."

"It's fun to trap wild animals," said Marsha.

"You bet!" agreed Jim.

"But trapping rabbits and puppies isn't any fun," remarked Marsha. "Not when we wanted a raccoon."

Marsha thought for a moment. Then she bent down and opened the door of the trap.

"Hey," shouted Jim in a surprised voice. "What are you doing?"

"It's cruel to keep a raccoon trapped," replied Marsha. "Besides, if this one has babies, they might die without her."

The raccoon looked up at the children through her black, furry mask. "She's trying to say, 'Thanks,'" explained Jim. "This raccoon would have made a good pet."

"Maybe," answered Marsha, watching the animal disappear into the woods. "But she makes a better wild animal. She knows where she belongs."

Only My Opinion

Is a caterpillar ticklish?
    Well, it's always my belief
That he giggles, as he wiggles
    Across a hairy leaf.

Monica Shannon

Fuzzy Wuzzy, Creepy Crawly

Fuzzy wuzzy, creepy crawly
    Caterpillar funny,
You will be a butterfly
    When the days are sunny.

Winging, flinging, dancing, springing
    Butterfly so yellow,
You were once a caterpillar,
    Wriggly, wiggly fellow.

Lillian Schulz Vanada

Butterfly

As I walked through my garden
I saw a butterfly light on a flower.
His wings were pink and purple:
He spoke a small word . . .
It was *Follow!*
"I cannot follow"
I told him,
"I have to go the opposite way."

Hilda Conkling

The Magic
of the Monarch

The monarch butterfly is one of the most beautiful of all insects. It begins its life as a tiny egg laid on a leaf of a milkweed plant. A few days after the egg is laid, a caterpillar begins to form. When it has grown large enough, the caterpillar hatches and comes out of the shell.

From the moment it hatches, the caterpillar spends its life eating and growing. First it eats its own eggshell. Then it starts eating its way from leaf to leaf until it is full grown. The caterpillar's skin does not grow. As it becomes too small, the skin cracks and comes off. A monarch caterpillar sheds its skin five times during its life.

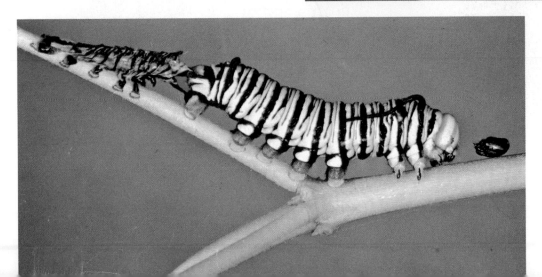

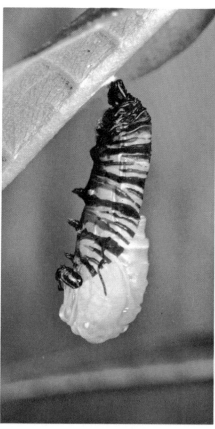

After it has reached full growth, the monarch caterpillar begins the next stage of its life. It spins a "button" of silk on a twig or a leaf. There it hangs, head down, swinging freely from a silken thread. At this time the caterpillar sheds its skin for the last time and forms another shell around its body.

Then a wonderful change begins to take place. The shell around the caterpillar's body, called a chrysalis, takes on a shiny green color.

In about eight days the color of the chrysalis begins to change. And inside, where no one can watch, the monarch caterpillar is turning into a beautiful orange and black monarch butterfly.

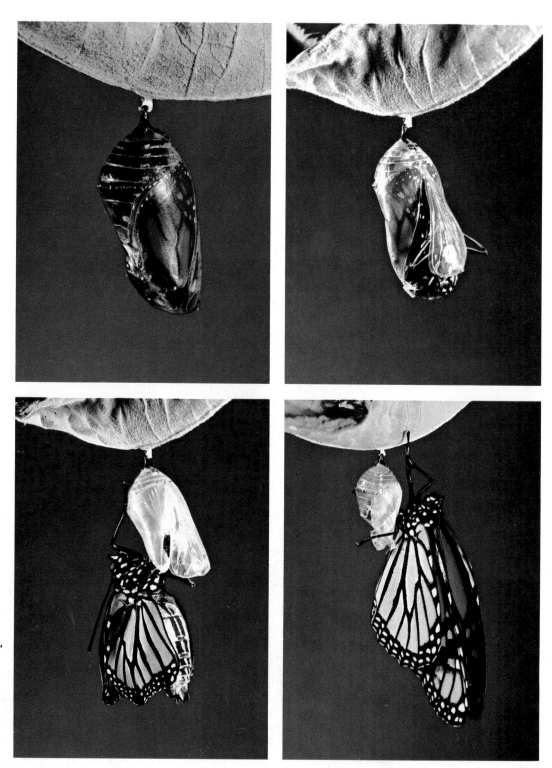

230

At just the right moment the chrysalis cracks open, and little by little, the monarch crawls out. For several hours it hangs onto the swinging chrysalis, waiting for its wings to dry. Then, as if by magic, the monarch butterfly spreads its wings and is ready for its first flight.

Why does the caterpillar spin a silken thread?
What is the magic of the monarch?

A Good
Morning's Work

Mitsuo Yamada leaned on his hoe and sighed deeply. "It will be a long, long day," he said to himself.

"Mitsuo! Mitsuo, have you started to clear the weeds?" his father called.

Hurriedly Mitsuo raised the hoe and called out, "I have begun, Father."

Mitsuo looked at the hoe as it sank into the soft brown earth. "I have begun," he said to himself. Pulling as hard as he could, he cut a long path through the green of the weeds.

Again Mitsuo lifted the hoe. But instead of chopping among the weeds, he dropped the hoe and bent down. He parted the grass and discovered a spider spinning its web on the leaves of a milkweed. Raindrops had caught on the silken threads, and each drop was shining like a sun.

"Mitsuo!"

"I am cutting weeds," Mitsuo called as the hoe fell sharply to the ground.

"One milkweed cannot matter," Mitsuo said to himself. "And I would like to see a thousand suns shining from this web every morning."

He began to labor once more. Carefully he cut other plants away until the milkweed stood alone, the web shining with many tiny suns.

"Mitsuo!"

"I have begun, Father." And the hoe rose and fell, rose and fell.

"Cr-r-r-oak!"

Mitsuo stopped and listened. He heard nothing except the lazy sounds of morning. Once again he raised the hoe.

"Cr-r-r-oak!"

"Again I think I have heard a frog," said Mitsuo. "But that is impossible. A pond is not here. Where the willow dips its leaves is where the frog should sing."

"Cr-r-r-oak!"

Mitsuo again raised his hoe, but he did not raise it to chop weeds. Instead, he held it just high enough to separate the weeds so that he could see what was hidden beneath them.

There was a puddle of water, but it was not big enough for a big frog. The puddle was just big enough for a frog until it grew larger.

"There must be a frog," said Mitsuo. "Did I not hear the song it sang? Why is there no frog to be seen?"

"Cr-r-r-oak!"

Mitsuo looked as hard as he could. Then he saw the frog. Its round eyes were shining up at him.

"Cr-r-r-oak!"

"Frog, sir," said Mitsuo, "you are in the Yamada vegetable garden. If you stay in your water, where will the Yamada tomatoes come from when summer is here?"

"Cr-r-r-oak!" said the frog.

"Of course," said Mitsuo, "if I did not eat tomatoes every Tuesday, we would not need to plant so many. Then you could stay in your own little puddle."

"Cr-r-r-oak!" said the frog.

"I will do this," said Mitsuo. He pulled the hoe back and let the weeds close over the frog's home.

Then Mitsuo labored hard to cut away the weeds, but he left enough of them to hide the puddle where the frog lived.

Mitsuo leaned on his hoe. "How fine it looks," he said. "It is like a pond where the best frogs are to be found."

"Cr-r-r-oak!" said the frog.

"Mitsuo!"

"I am working, Father." Mitsuo's hoe went up and down, up and down, with great speed.

Then Mitsuo stopped again. He looked at the purple and yellow and orange flowers. It didn't matter that they were flowering weeds. They were flowers to Mitsuo. And over the flowers there was the lazy sound of bees.

"Mitsuo! Mitsuo!" his father called.

Mitsuo did not answer.

"Mitsuo!" repeated his father.

"I am doing what I should, Father." But Mitsuo's hoe did not cut into the field of flowers.

"I cannot cut the flowers now," Mitsuo said to himself. "The bees need them to make their honey. It would not be good for the Yamadas if the bees did not have flowers from which to make honey. The Yamadas would then have to go without honey all winter. Would it not be better to leave the flowers for the bees? But if I leave the flowers, will there be enough land left for the vegetables?"

Mitsuo looked at the garden.

"There will be enough," he said. "Anyway, I can always give up beans on Wednesday."

"Mitsuo!"

"I am working, Father!" And he was. Mitsuo pretended that he was a machine working with great speed. He cut his way through the weeds, leaving narrow rows of brown earth.

But what machine could stop and see what Mitsuo saw? Could a machine see a chrysalis that had cracked open and was swinging by its silken thread? Could a machine see a butterfly coming out of the chrysalis? Could a machine watch the butterfly unfold its wings in the drying heat of the sun?

Never had a boy been as careful as Mitsuo Yamada. His hoe tiptoed about the plant. Not even a shadow fell across the butterfly. The butterfly moved its wings to the feel of the air, but it did not notice Mitsuo.

When Mitsuo saw how many weeds remained, he shook his head and said to himself, "I will have to cut down more weeds. The butterfly will fly away, but there will be other butterflies."

Just then sunlight showed each color of the butterfly's wings.

"No!" Mitsuo shook his head. "There will be many butterflies, but there will never be another one like this. I will work twice as hard and twice as fast."

Mitsuo labored with such speed that he might not have seen the nest in the grass, if he hadn't been a boy. It was the smallest of nests, and in it was a tiny bird. The bird did not fly off, although it was afraid of Mitsuo.

"I will not hurt your eggs. You are bravest of all birds. From the eggs in your nest will hatch eagles."

"Tweet," said the bird.

"No, no, little bird," said Mitsuo. "I did not mean real eagles. Like you, the birds that hatch will be small. And I, Mitsuo Yamada, will not break apart your nest."

"Tweet," said the bird.

"Mitsuo!"

"I am working, Father."

The bird's bright eyes followed Mitsuo as he chopped around and around its nest. The weeds fell under his hoe until a band of clear ground separated the bird and Mitsuo.

When the bird saw that Mitsuo meant no harm to it nor to its eggs, it flew about Mitsuo's head as if to thank him.

"That is right," said Mitsuo. "When someone does a good deed, it is your duty to say, 'Thanks.'"

"Mitsuo!"

Mitsuo lifted his hoe. "I am working, Father."

"Come. It is time to eat."

Mitsuo was always ready to eat. He put the hoe over his shoulder and started to leave the field. But before he left, he turned once to look at the amount of work he had done.

There was the milkweed where the silken web had caught a thousand suns.

There the land was cleared, except for the place where the frog had made a pond of its own from a rain puddle.

There in the middle of the cleared earth some flowers grew, busy with bees.

And there was the butterfly. Mitsuo would remember its wings in the sunlight long after it flew away.

"Tweet," said the bird in its flight around Mitsuo.

Mitsuo nodded his head. "It was a good morning's work," he said, "a good morning's work, indeed!"

The eagle speaks

The sun's rays
Lie along my wings
And stretch beyond their tips.

A little gray whirlwind
Is trying to catch me.
Across my path
It keeps whirling.

Papago

Kiya,
the Gull

Kiya was a free bird. From sunrise till sunset he circled above the sand and the sea with the other sea gulls, searching for food. He kept a close eye on the wharf to pick up after the fishermen.

On the beach he watched while the children had their picnics, and he ate the sandwiches they couldn't finish. When he came too close, the children cried, "Look! Look at the sea gull!"

After a storm Kiya and the other gulls cleaned up the shore. They ate almost anything and were still hungry.

One morning Kiya began the day before the sun was up. He left the little island where he lived and went to the wharf. He wanted to be there when the fishermen came in to clean the fish, but this morning no one was around.

Just then Kiya spotted a bundle of seaweed tangled in a length of wire. It had been washed ashore and promised a picnic of delicious food.

Kiya circled over the bundle, and when he found it quite safe, he fell to work. He pecked at the weeds with his bill. The more he pecked, the more he found.

But the wire got in his way. He had to untangle the straw and the seaweed before he could reach the crabs that hid within. He pushed at the wire until one end came free. Then Kiya stuck his head into the opening.

Other gulls noticed the flapping of Kiya's wings and came down to join him. Screaming and flapping their wings, the gulls pecked at the seaweed and pulled at the wire. They ate what they could find and then flew away. At that moment Kiya discovered that he was tangled.

"Kiya-kiya-kiya-kiya . . .," he cried.

The screams rang out across the beach. The more the gull struggled, the tighter the wire pulled around his body.

Finally he was able to free his wings, but the wire was still wrapped around him. One leg was held so tightly that he could not move it.

A boy was sitting in his boat watching the gulls. When he noticed Kiya struggling, he came ashore. Kiya saw him coming; he saw the boy reach out his hands. Kiya flapped his wings and lifted himself to safety, even though the wire cut into his back and leg. The boy ran after him, but Kiya rose out of his reach.

He glided over to the beach and came to rest
on the cool, hard sand at the water's edge. The
wire dragged on the ground behind him.

People were already on the beach for a day in
the sun. "Look at that gull!" someone cried.
"He's all caught up in something."

People ran toward Kiya. Hands reached for
him, but he hopped away on one leg. Then,
flapping his wings, Kiya was able to raise
himself off the ground again.

He flew to the high place where the gulls
came every noon. The other gulls were still away,
searching for their morning food.

Hungry as Kiya was, he hurt too much to fly. Suffering with pain, he wanted only to be left in peace. He settled on the highest spot he could find, where he could see in all directions. And there he rested.

Then a group of children came to climb the hills of sand. "Look!" they cried. "That sea gull is all tangled up."

Kiya watched as the children slowly made a circle around him. Closer and closer they crept until Kiya spread his wings and tried to fly. But the tangled wire cut into his sore body.

"Catch him!" cried the children.

Kiya was glad he had landed on the highest spot; from there he was able to rise above the children's hands. They leaped to catch at the swinging wire but missed. Kiya was already on his way.

After this narrow escape Kiya settled on the water where the cool waves lapped his cuts. Slowly he drifted out to sea. How was he going to rid himself of this wire? How was he going to find something to eat?

And then there was that boy again, bearing down on him in his boat! Kiya tried to swim away, but with only one leg kicking, it was hard to keep from going in circles. The boy brought his sailboat into the wind and drifted toward the tangled bird.

Kiya again saw two hands reaching for him. He beat his wings wildly, trying to rise above the water. The boat was at a standstill now, and Kiya was able to escape, dragging the wire behind him in the water.

Where could he go but back to his island? There were too many people on the beach who were always trying to catch him. In all his life no one had ever tried to do that before. Why were people so cruel now when he was suffering?

Kiya made a difficult landing on the roof of a deserted shed where he and the gulls liked to rest. At first the other gulls let Kiya have his favorite place. But when they saw his leg caught in the tangled wire and covered with blood, they looked at him with unfriendly eyes. He was not one of them anymore.

Another gull flew in and pushed against Kiya. Then all at once the other sea gulls turned on him and drove him from the shed. Still suffering with pain and dragging the wire behind him, Kiya hid in the salt grass.

Sometime later Kiya tried to reach the other side of the island, but the wire caught on a bush. He was held fast! The more he struggled, the tighter the wire became! By now he was too sore to move.

The sun was low in the west when the boat appeared, bringing the boy to the island. Kiya saw him come ashore, carrying a small pack. The boy went to the far side of the island where the other gulls were settling down for the night.

Kiya was well hidden where he was. It would soon be dark. If he didn't move, the boy would never find him.

But the boy returned and built a fire out of the driftwood he had gathered. Kiya watched as the fire burned brightly. He soon fell asleep, escaping from the suffering the day had brought.

During the night the gull woke to find the fire still glowing on the beach below. Toward morning the fire died out, but the boy still lay there sleeping in his blanket. Now was the time for Kiya to escape—before the boy woke and discovered that Kiya was there.

Kiya threw his weight against the wire and pushed with all his might. Wildly he beat his sore wings.

"Kiya-kiya-kiya-kiya." He repeated the cry over and over.

The cries woke the boy. He climbed the hill and stood above Kiya, just looking. They stared at one another, bird and boy, and Kiya knew his time had come. The gull pecked wildly at the reaching hand as it closed over his head.

"Easy now, easy," said the boy as he struggled with the tangled wire. Kiya gave up trying to fight. The boy unhooked the wire and drew it over the gull's head. Then he freed Kiya's leg. "Easy now," he repeated.

The gull lay still. Two hands lifted him carefully and set him on his feet.

Kiya put his weight on the sore leg. He took one step, then two. Although his leg was stiff, he found that he could walk. He stared at the boy standing above him. The hands weren't reaching for him anymore. Those hands had untangled the wire and had given him his freedom.

The boy asked, "Will you be all right?"

Kiya spread his wings and felt that he was free. When he flapped his wings, there was no dragging wire. Slowly he rose into the air and circled above the boy who was staring up at him. He remained a moment, enjoying the morning breeze. Then he glided down to the water and drifted awhile on the waves.

Why had he been so frightened of the boy with the reaching hands?

Kiya often flew over the wharf and the beach that summer. There were many boats. There were many boys. Was there one among them who had given him his freedom?

And the boy with the boat looked up and wondered. Of all those sea gulls circling above, was there one he knew? Which one had he saved?

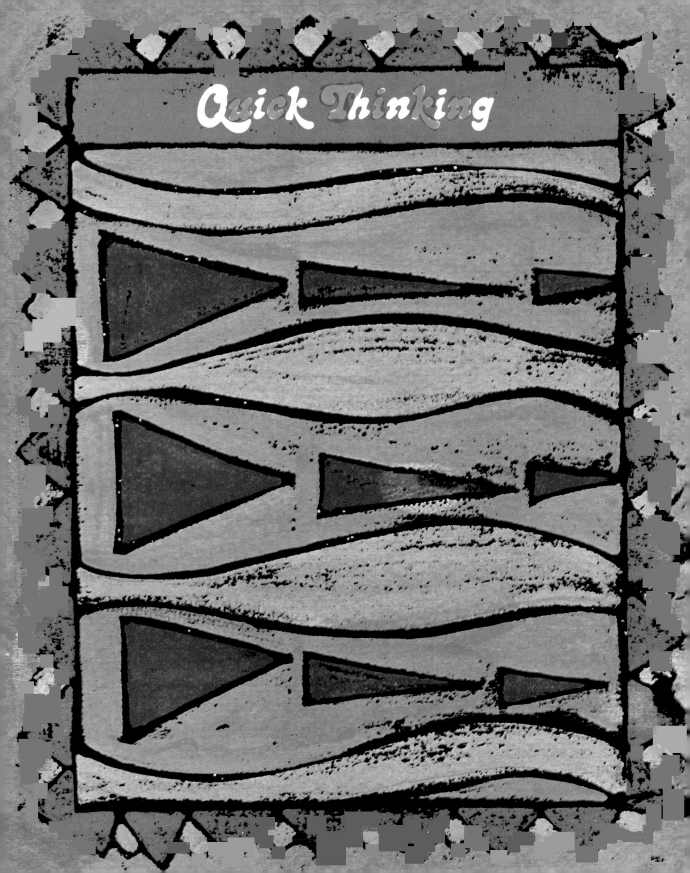

Steve's Clue

Steve Jackson gave the ball another bounce. Then he turned to look at his friend, Don Sharp, who was coming up the walk.

"I suppose you've heard the bad news," said Steve as Don sat down on the porch steps.

Don nodded. "It's the second gas-station robbery in less than a week. Did they get our Scout money?"

"Every cent of it," Steve answered sadly. "The last member paid me his money yesterday. I was afraid I might lose it, so I took it to the gas station where the Scout leader works. Now the money's all gone. Over four hundred dollars!"

Just then the door opened, and Mrs. Jackson appeared with a plate of sandwiches, some cookies, and some cherry pop. "I thought a picnic lunch would make you feel better," she said. "Don't give up hope about the money. The police might catch the robber." She went back into the house and closed the screen door behind her.

"Do they have any idea who took the money?" asked Don. "I wonder if it was the same person who robbed the other gas station."

"I don't honestly think they'll ever find out," remarked Steve. "This is the busiest time of the season. People come to the lake by the thousands. Could be any one of them. Anyway, every cent of our Scout money is gone."

Steve and Don were upset for a good reason. The Scouts had arranged to give five young boys from the children's home a vacation at the lake. The Scouts had just finished raising the amount of money needed. Now, on account of the robbery, the young boys wouldn't get a vacation after all.

Suddenly a black and white dog came around the corner of the house. He ran up to Steve and sniffed the cookies.

"No, Sport! Not for you," said Steve.

Then the big dog grabbed the ball and dashed toward the gate.

"Come back with that ball!" shouted Steve as he jumped up and raced after the dog. With his eyes on Sport, Steve ran through the gate and crashed into a red-haired man who was walking along the road. The man had a fishing pole and a dip net in one hand and a tackle box in the other.

The force of the crash knocked the tackle box out of the man's hand. With an angry roar, he dropped the pole and the net and grabbed wildly at the tackle box.

"You careless fool!" the man shouted. "See what you did! You should have a good beating. Get out of here before I —"

He raised his hand as if to strike, but a low growl stopped him. Sport had returned with the ball. He dropped it at Steve's feet and turned to face the red-haired man. The dog stiffened and growled deep in his throat. Steve grabbed Sport's collar just as he was ready to strike.

"Get that dog out of my way," yelled the man. Holding the tackle box carefully, he picked up the fishing pole and the net and walked on.

"Wow!" said Don. "Why was he so angry?"

"I don't know," answered Steve, picking up the ball and leading Sport inside the yard. Then he carefully locked the gate. "I never saw that fellow before, but there's something about him that seems familiar. I can't think what it is. And why was he so careful with that tackle box? He acted as though it might break."

Don nodded. "I noticed that, too. There must have been something in the box besides fishing tackle. I wonder if he really was going fishing."

For a moment the boys were quiet, thoughts spinning around in their head. "Let's find out," Steve said. "Let's take the path leading across the meadow and down the hill to the lake. If we hurry, we can get there ahead of him. Then we'll know whether he's really going fishing. Come on!"

With Don close behind, Steve raced along the path. They reached the hilltop and started down the other side where the path curved around an old, deserted house.

Suddenly Steve stopped. "Duck behind these bushes," he whispered. "And keep quiet. He's behind that old house."

Don dropped to the ground and crawled up beside Steve. Separating the branches, he peeked through. The red-haired man kept looking around. Then he picked up a spade and started digging.

263

"What's he looking for?" asked Don, his lips close to Steve's ear. "No one has lived in that house for years. And where did he get that spade?"

"I saw him come out of the cellar," Steve whispered back. "I wonder how he knew the spade was down there. He might be digging for bait, but I don't think so."

As the boys watched, the man looked around. Then he opened the tackle box and pulled out a package which he placed in the hole. He covered it with a spadeful of dirt and tossed some twigs and leaves on top.

"Now I remember!" whispered Steve. "I know why he seems so familiar. His gold teeth! I noticed them when he yelled at me. He has two gold teeth right in the front of his mouth. So did another man I saw last week. And both men had tackle boxes with bent-in corners. Let's get out of here!"

They headed for home, crawling along until they were safely out of the man's sight. Then they stood up and ran as fast as they could.

In a matter of minutes the boys were sitting on Steve's porch. "What were you talking about back at the deserted house?" asked Don. "What other man?"

"Last Wednesday I was on my way to the Scout meeting. I met a man carrying a fishing pole and a tackle box with a bent-in corner. He had two gold teeth. But his hair was gray, not red."

Steve was quiet for a moment. Then he said, "Wait a minute! That was the same day the first gas station was robbed. Do you suppose that man was wearing a wig?"

"Maybe you've got something!" shouted Don. "Let's go tell the police."

They soon reached the police station, where the captain listened to their story. "Sounds possible," he said when the boys had finished. "You fellows go back home. We'll take over."

An hour later a police car drove up to the Jackson home. Don and Steve were sitting on the front steps, waiting for news.

"We got him!" said the captain, coming up the walk. "He was at the deserted house, and some of the stolen money was still in the tackle box. The package with the rest of the money was right where you told us it would be. Every cent has been returned, and the fellow is in jail, thanks to you boys."

"What about his hair?" Steve asked.

"A wig! Just as you thought. The gray hair was a wig, too. His own hair is brown." The policeman smiled. "Listen to the news tonight. We're going to tell how you boys helped to solve the case. There's a nice reward, too."

The boys waved as the police car drove off.

"Hey!" said Don. "We solved that mystery just like real detectives."

Steve nodded. "But the best part is that those kids from the children's home will get to have a nice vacation."

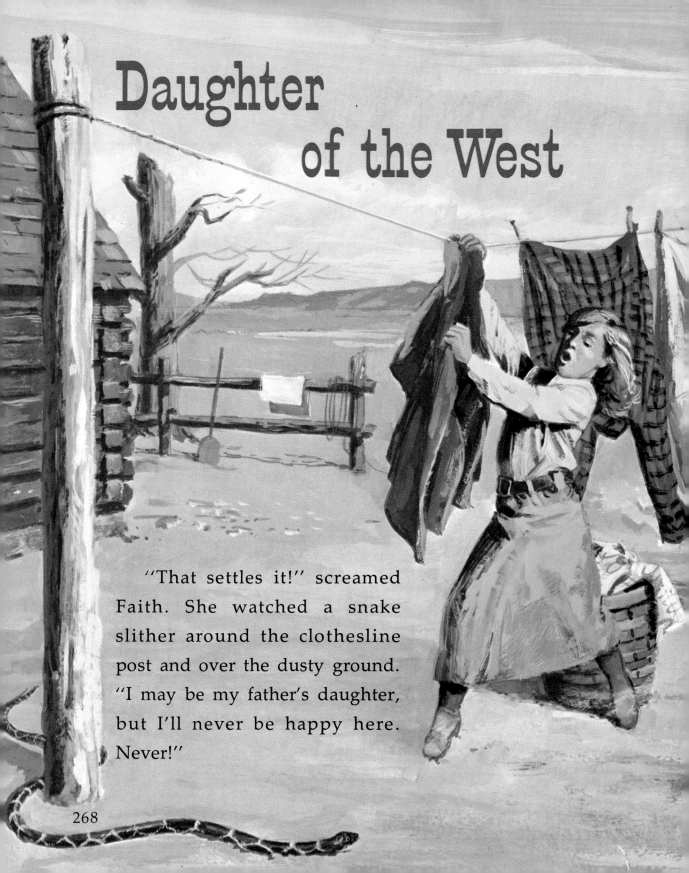

Daughter of the West

"That settles it!" screamed Faith. She watched a snake slither around the clothesline post and over the dusty ground. "I may be my father's daughter, but I'll never be happy here. Never!"

Taking a quick look around, Faith frowned at the tiny cabin and the dusty yard. As far as she could see, there wasn't another human being in sight. Even Homer, the old workhorse, had gone with her father to a neighbor's ranch.

She pushed her long hair out of her eyes. And then she saw it again—that terrible, slithering snake!

Faith shuddered, thinking about the first day she and her father had been in this awful desert. They had spent the day shopping in town, and it was dark when they were ready to head for home.

Placing the packages in the back of the wagon, they had climbed onto the seat. Suddenly they heard a sound behind them—the rattle of a snake!

They were afraid to move for fear the snake might strike. It was dark. There was no moon, and they could not see. After what had seemed like hours, a shadowy form walked toward them. It was Jeb Peters, carrying a lantern. The light from the lantern frightened the snake, and it slithered out of sight.

Faith had not forgotten how frightened she was that night. But her fear was even greater now, for she was all alone. How she hated living in the desert with the heat, and the dust, and the hard labor! Most of all she hated feeling so lonely. The nearest neighbors lived half a mile away.

Faith never moved, watching as the snake slithered under a bush. She was sure it would strike at any moment. If she tried, she could barely reach the dinner bell near the back stoop. She wouldn't have to move much.

"Three rings of the dinner bell is a sign of trouble," her father had told her. So Faith clanged the bell once. She counted to five and clanged it again. She counted to five and clanged it a third time.

The snake was lazily sunning itself near the shed when Faith's father and Jeb Peters came running on foot. They hadn't even taken the time to saddle their horses. Her father took one look at the sleeping snake and let out an angry cry.

"You mean that's the reason you called us?" he shouted. "That snake's as harmless as a rabbit." And he shooed the snake away with a wave of his arms.

Faith was still shuddering with fear. Why was her father **so** cruel? Suddenly she wanted **to** get away. She didn't care **where.** Just away. She whirled **around** and ran. Her father called **after** her, "Wait, Faith, wait!" But **she** kept running, blinded by **her** tears.

She ran until she was **out of** breath. Then she fell to the **dusty** ground. Tears streamed from **her** eyes as though they would **never** stop.

Several minutes passed **by** before Faith quieted **down.** Suddenly she sat up. **Was** someone calling for help? **The** voice sounded familiar, and **it** seemed to be coming from **the** Peters' ranch. She jumped **to her** feet and ran. The cry **was** coming from the shed.

"It's Seth," she thought, dashing through the door. There he was, lying on the dirt floor. A heavy worktable lay across his body, and his leg was covered with blood.

"What happened?" asked Faith.

"I was climbing up to get the saddle for my pony," he answered, "and the table broke. I cut my leg on the ax when I fell."

"I'll help you," she said, moving the ax out of the way.

How pale Seth was! Faith looked around for something to use for a bandage. Finding a piece of cloth on a nearby shelf, she tied it around the boy's cut leg.

"Where's your mother?" she asked.

"She took some sandwiches to the men," replied Seth.

"Don't worry," said Faith. "I'll get help."

She looked toward the back porch and saw the dinner bell. "Oh, please, let them know they've got to come again!" She clanged the bell as loudly as possible.

Without waiting another moment, Faith climbed on Seth's pony and rode bareback as fast as she could.

Faith hadn't gone far when she saw Mr. Peters, her father, and another rancher riding toward her. Mrs. Peters was following close behind.

"There's been an accident," Faith cried. "Seth fell on the ax. He's in the shed." With that the men raced past her.

By the time she and Mrs. Peters reached the shed, the men had Seth in the wagon. "He's in pretty good condition," called one man.

"We're taking him to the doctor," added Mr. Peters. "The ax was sharp, but the cut looks worse than it really is."

Faith's father walked over and lifted her off the pony. "I'm sorry about this morning," she said.

"I know," he replied. "I forgot how scared you are of snakes. It's pretty rough out here in the middle of the desert, and I realize what a hardship it is for you with no mo—"

"But I've got you," replied Faith before he could finish his sentence.

He put his hand on Faith's shoulder. "I heard some good news this morning, Faith girl. There's going to be a big, new dam built across the river. That'll mean irrigation for us ranchers. Building the dam will be a big task, but irrigation will mean lots and lots of water! Good crops, and a little money ahead. Why, honey, in a few years this desert is going to be as green as our front yard back East! There's going to be beauty all around us."

"I don't care what happens, good or bad," said Faith as she hugged her father. "I'm not going to run away from anything again."

Just then Mrs. Peters hurried up to them. "The men told me about the bandage on Seth's leg, and how you came to his aid. I hope to do a good deed for you someday."

"It didn't seem like much," replied Faith. "My father taught me how to make a bandage."

"You've got a real head on you," said Mrs. Peters. "You're a true daughter of the West."

Faith smiled. "I like that, Mrs. Peters. 'A true daughter of the West.'"

The Jewelry Store Robbery

"And now an important message from the police." Harry listened carefully to the evening news. "Jansen's Jewelry Store has just been added to the growing list of robberies here in Center City. Anyone who can help in this matter is asked to call this special number, Hunter 5-12—"

Harry switched off the TV, put on his jacket, and left the apartment. Before long he arrived at the police station where his uncle worked as a detective.

"Hi, Uncle Pat," he said.

"Can't take time to talk now," replied his uncle, hurrying toward the door. "There's been another robbery."

"I know," said Harry. "I just heard the message on TV. Can I go with you? Please! I promise to stay out of the way."

"Well, I suppose," answered his uncle. "You won't be in any danger now."

They left the office and hopped into a waiting police car. With lights flashing and the siren blowing, the car raced down the street at top speed. In less than five minutes Harry and his uncle were in front of the jewelry store.

"Looks like the robber broke the glass to unlock the door," said Harry, pointing to the pieces of glass on the sidewalk. Uncle Pat didn't say a word.

Together they entered the jewelry store. "I'm Detective Rule," Harry's uncle told the man behind the counter. "Are you Mr. Jansen?"

The jeweler nodded and said, "Thank you for coming."

"What happened?" asked Detective Rule.

Mr. Jansen swallowed hard. "All the clerks had gone home, and I had locked up the store. I was in the back room doing some paper work when I heard a loud crash. I jumped up and rushed into the store. I tried to switch on the lights, but they didn't work. At the same moment I saw a man run out the front door. I followed him, but he disappeared around the corner."

"What did he look like?"

"I wish I knew," answered Mr. Jansen. "Wait, perhaps I do. Yesterday one of the clerks noticed a man standing in front of the shop, looking at the jewelry and talking to himself. The clerk pointed the man out to me. I wondered what he was up to, so I took a closer look. He was in his fifties, about six feet tall, and neatly dressed. Maybe he was the one who stole the jewelry."

"Do you have a list of what was stolen?" questioned Detective Rule.

"Right here," answered Mr. Jansen.

The jeweler reached behind the counter and picked up a sheet of paper. "You'll notice that only the best pieces of jewelry were taken," he said, handing the list to Harry's uncle.

"You said you tried to switch on the lights—but they didn't work?" questioned Detective Rule.

"That's right," replied Mr. Jansen. "Later I realized that the fuse had been taken out."

"Will you please remove the fuse? asked Harry's uncle. "I'd like to get a better idea of how the store looked at the time of the robbery."

"Gladly," replied Mr. Jansen. "But I have to go into the back room to do it."

When the jeweler headed for the fuse box, Harry realized something was strange about the story. "I know who took the jewelry!" he whispered excitedly.

Uncle Pat smiled. "You'd make a good detective," he said. "But you should have been able to solve the case in front of the shop."

See If You Can Tell

Why did Detective Rule say that Harry should have been able to solve the case in front of the shop?

Who do you think stole the jewelry?

Answer

Harry had pointed to the glass on the sidewalk in front of the shop door. If the door had been broken from the outside, the glass would have fallen inside the shop. When Detective Rule asked the jeweler to take out the fuse, Mr. Jansen gave himself away. A robber could not have removed the fuse without being seen because the fuse box was in the back room where Mr. Jansen had been working. So Mr. Jansen was the one who stole the jewelry.

No One Heard Him Call

He went down to the woodshed
To put his bike away.
There was no moon. There were no stars.
He ran the whole dark way.
And when he hurried back again
The porch light had gone out!
He couldn't find the doorknob,
So then he gave a shout.

It wasn't very loud, though,
And no one heard him call.
He pounded with his knuckles;
Still no one came at all.
But then where he was standing
A *light* came streaming wide:
"My goodness, is that you?" she said.
And he was safe inside!

Dorothy Aldis

285

ADVENTURE AT THE OLD MILL

April ran up the steps to the big, white house and rapped several times. The door opened, and a neatly dressed man stared at her. His face didn't look at all familiar.

"What do you want?" he snapped.

"I—I came to see Granny Wilson," replied April.

"She's not seeing anybody," he answered, starting to shut the door.

"But Granny told me to be sure and stop on my way home from school today," explained April. "She's making a rag doll for my little sister."

The man turned and spoke to someone in the house. Then he opened the door wider. "The doctor says you can come in for a minute," he growled. "Mrs. Wilson is sick, and we're going to take her to the hospital. So make it snappy."

From where she was standing, April could see the large form of a man standing near Granny. He looked up as April entered the room. "Come in," he said crossly.

"I'm glad he's not my doctor," thought April, brushing past him. Then she said, "Hello, Granny. I'm sorry you're sick."

The white-haired lady smiled weakly. April felt terrible when she saw how pale Granny was. April and her brother, Jake, loved Mrs. Wilson as though she were their own grandmother.

"You can stay only a minute," said the doctor, dropping into a chair beside the bed.

"The doll is almost finished," said Granny.

"Don't worry about it," April told her. "Jake and I will come to see you in the —"

"She's not going to the hospital here in Jamestown," said the doctor. "We're taking her to the one in Cherry City. Then her nephew is taking her on a vacation. Isn't that right, Granny?"

The white-haired lady waited a moment, then nodded her head. "Yes, my nephew has decided I need a rest."

April didn't understand. She was sure Granny had told her that every single member of her family had died. "I didn't know you had a nephew, Granny."

"Ben's your long-lost nephew, isn't he, Granny?" asked the doctor.

Again Mrs. Wilson waited a moment before agreeing. Then she picked up the rag doll and turned to April. "Just a few more stitches, and it will be ready," she said.

"I'll finish it for you," offered April.

"No," Granny said quickly. "I promised." The thread flew in and out as she began to sew on the doll's head.

When she had finished sewing, she broke the thread and handed the rag doll to April. "Tell Toodles to be careful not to rip the stitches," she warned.

April looked surprised and started to speak, but
something made her keep still. Instead she thanked
Granny and hurried out of the house. She almost
ran into Jake who was walking lazily up the
driveway.

"Hey, look out!" shouted her brother.

"Don't go in there," warned April.

"What do you mean?" asked Jake. "Granny
gave me a list of things she wants done today. I'm
supposed to mail a package and then go to the
library."

So April told him what had happened. "If you ask me, there's something funny about that nephew—and the doctor, too." Then she added with a shudder, "But I guess Granny is sick. She can't even remember people's names. She told me to give this doll to Toodles and for her not to rip the stitches!"

"Toodles? Why, Granny knows that's our dog's name!"

"Maybe that's what's wrong," said April. "Maybe she's beginning to forget things."

They walked silently toward home, feeling sorry for their good friend.

When Saturday came they missed going over to help her. So, while their parents and younger sister were at the market, April and Jake decided to have a picnic in the yard. Afterwards April lay down on the grass to rest. The rag doll on the porch caught her eye.

"Jake, how do you suppose Granny's nephew found her?" she asked.

"I don't know. Maybe he heard about her money and came to see her."

"You mean you believe all those tales about Granny hiding every cent of her money around the house?" asked April.

"Oh, sure," he said. "I bet there's a secret hiding place in the cellar. Why not make it a real mystery? Suppose that man isn't her nephew at all. Suppose he's going to force Granny ——"

"Don't be silly," replied April. "I talked to Granny myself, and she'd have told me if anything was wrong." Then April's eyes grew big and round. "Oh, Jake, what if Granny was afraid they'd hurt me if she said anything? What if they were planning to steal her money?"

"Now who's being silly?" he questioned.

"Just the same, I'm going back to see if Granny's gone to the hospital! Are you coming?"

"OK, Miss Detective," said Jake with a teasing smile.

April was uneasy. And when they rapped again and again on Granny's front door, and there was no answer, she felt even worse.

"Poor Granny," April remarked sadly. "She must be in the hospital by now."

When they reached home, Jake tossed the rag doll to April. "Better take this before Toodles rips out the stitches."

April caught the doll and stood there looking at it. "Granny knew me when I was there."

"So what?"

"Well, maybe she was trying to tell me something when she said not to let Toodles rip the stitches."

"Forget it," answered Jake. "You're just making something out of nothing."

"Now wait! Granny had finished sewing the doll and she — That's it!" April started to pull at the doll's head.

"Hey, what are you doing?" yelled Jake.

April paid no attention to her brother as she ripped the threads. She pulled out the cotton stuffing, and a piece of paper fell to the ground. She picked it up. No writing. No message. Just a rough map with a drawing of an old building. She was disappointed.

294

"That looks like the old mill," said Jake.

"So who wants a map showing the old mill?" snapped April.

"What a place to hide out!" said Jake.

"That's it!" cried his sister. "Granny was trying to give me a message. She must have stuck the map in the doll's head before she sewed it shut. Come on—let's go!"

"Go? Where?"

"To the old mill, silly. Granny was trying to tell me where those men were taking her."

"You don't know that for sure," Jake said. "And if you're right, we ought to tell the police about the map."

"We can't call them until we know for certain."

"I still say we should call the police," said Jake. "They'd know what to do."

"Let's make sure Granny's there," begged April. "Then we'll call the police. We've got to try to rescue her."

Jake finally agreed. So, after leaving a message for their parents, the children headed for the old mill road.

A Close Call

It had already begun to get dark when they reached the woods. "I can't see an inch ahead of me. Ouch!" cried April, rubbing her scratched leg. "Maybe we should go back."

"We're almost there now," remarked Jake. "Besides, it was your idea to rescue Granny. Remember?"

April nodded. Just then she saw the old mill standing like a tall ghost against the night sky. She could hear the creaking of the wheel.

"Look!" hissed Jake in her ear. "I see a car parked over there."

"Let's go back," whispered April. "This place is spooky!"

"Think about Granny. We still don't know if she's in there."

"I'm scared!" said April.

"Aw—come on. I'll go first."

April followed her brother's shadow up to the old building. "There's a light," she said, pointing to a small window high on one side.

"Shhhh!" warned Jake. "I'm going to get on that branch by the window so I can see inside."

But the tree trunk was too smooth and the branch too high.

"Help me up," he said. "Then I'll give you a hand."

Soon both children had edged their way along the branch and were near the window. Suddenly the branch began to creak and bend.

"Go back!" Jake whispered excitedly.

But his warning came too late. Crack! The branch broke, and the children fell to the ground. As they lay there frightened but not hurt, a door banged open, and a lantern shined pools of yellow light on the ground.

"Oooh!" groaned April.

Jake clapped his hand over her mouth. She started to pull away, then froze. A man held the lantern high and looked around. It was Granny's nephew!

"Nothing here," he called back. "Some animal in the brush, I guess."

"Well, bring that lantern back," another voice answered.

The door slammed shut, and everything was dark again.

"Wow! That was a close call," whispered April.

"Now I know something's wrong," said Jake. "There's a door in the back of the mill near the wheel. Let's see if it's open."

Quietly they headed toward the creaking, old wheel. Water dripped on them as they pushed open the door. Once inside, they hid behind some huge barrels that were piled on top of one another.

"I'll see if I can peek around these," whispered April, getting to her feet. She crept toward the end barrel and leaned forward just as a spider web touched her face. Jumping back, she banged into Jake and sent him flying. The barrels came falling down all around them.

"What have we here?" said a rough voice. "You got careless, kid, and we caught you."

April, still hidden behind two barrels, peeked out. The nephew had Jake by the shoulder, and the doctor was leading Granny by the arm.

"Who's with you?" the nephew demanded of Jake.

"I'm — Just me," answered Jake in a shaky voice.

"Take a look around, Ben," said the doctor. "I'll keep these two quiet."

April felt as if freezing water were dripping down her neck. She watched Granny's nephew coming toward her. Carefully she crawled into one of the barrels and lay still. Heavy footsteps passed and then returned a minute later.

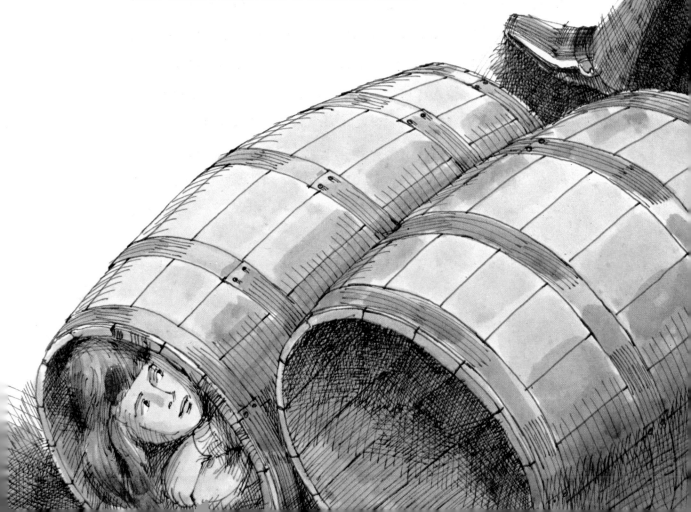

"No one around," said Ben. "There's a little door back there where the kid got in. Better make the lady tell where her money is."

"Not here," said the doctor. "We'll take her somewhere else. The kid, too—in case he was followed."

April shuddered. Her heart began to sink when she realized they were about to leave. How could she rescue Granny and Jake by herself?

Suddenly April had an idea. She stood up and gave one barrel a big push. It hit the nephew, and his feet flew out from under him. Another barrel caught the doctor behind his knees and sent him falling to the floor.

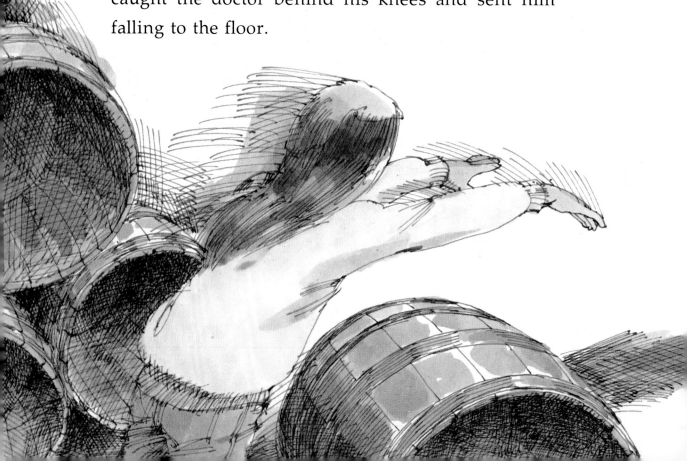

"Run, Granny! Run, Jake!" screamed April, pushing one barrel after another.

Suddenly a siren was heard outside. A door to the mill was pushed open, and in dashed their father with the police.

April could hardly believe her eyes. Everything was going to be all right now. Granny would be safe.

After April and Jake explained what had happened, they were more than glad to see the police lead the men away.

"Honestly!" said Granny. "They thought I had money hidden someplace. My money is in the bank where it belongs." She smiled at April and Jake. "I happen to keep a few dollars at home though—enough to reward you for rescuing me."

"You don't have to do that," said April. "We're glad we could help."

"Sure," agreed Jake. "And look at the fun we had solving a real mystery of our own."

GLOSSARY

The glossary can help you find out the pronunciations and meanings of some of the words used in this book.

The pronunciation is shown after the word in this way: **a board** (ə bôrd'). The letters and signs are pronounced as shown in the pronunciation key. This key will help you to pronounce the words that are in the glossary.

FULL PRONUNCIATION KEY*

a	hat, cap	j	jam, enjoy	u	cup, butter
ā	age, face	k	kind, seek	ů	full, put
ä	father, far	l	land, coal	ü	rule, move
b	bad, rob	m	me, am	v	very, save
ch	child, much	n	no, in	w	will, woman
d	did, red	ng	long, bring	y	young, yet
e	let, best	o	hot, rock	z	zero, breeze
ē	equal, be	ō	open, go	zh	measure, seizure
er	term, learn	ô	order, all		
f	fat, if	oi	oil, voice		
g	go, bag	ou	house, out		
h	he, how	p	paper, cup		
i	it, pin	r	run, try		
ī	ice, five	s	say, yes		
		sh	she, rush		
		t	tell, it		
		th	thin, both		
		ŦH	then, smooth		

ə represents:
- a in about
- e in taken
- i in pencil
- o in lemon
- u in circus

*From THORNDIKE-BARNHART BEGINNING DICTIONARY by E. L. Thorndike and Clarence L. Barnhart. Copyright © 1972 by Scott, Foresman and Company. Reprinted by permission of the publisher.

305

A a

a board (ə bôrd′), to be on or in an airplane, a bus, a ship, or a train.

a larm (ə lärm′), **1** a device that makes a noise to waken or to warn. **2** the fear caused by a feeling of danger.

al low (ə lou′), **1** to permit. **2** to give.

ar range (ə rānj′), **1** to put into proper order. **2** to make plans for.

a shore (ə shôr′), **1** on the land. **2** to the land.

ax or **axe** (aks), a tool having a sharp blade fastened to a handle, used for cutting or for chopping wood.

B b

beast (bēst), any four-footed animal.

be have (bi hāv′), **1** to act in a certain way. **2** to act properly.

blind (blīnd), unable to see.

board[1] (bôrd), a wide piece of wood used for building.

board[2] (bôrd), to go onto an airplane, a bus, a ship, or a train.

boast (bōst), **1** to brag about. **2** to be proud of.

breeze (brēz), a gentle wind.

C c

cab in (kab′ ən), **1** a small, one-story house usually built of wood. **2** a room on a boat or ship for one or more persons.

clerk (klėrk), a person who sells goods in a shop or store.

com pa ny (kum′ pə nē), **1** a group of people joined together for a reason. **2** one or more guests.

con tin ue (kən tin′ yü), **1** to carry on or to keep up. **2** to go on with a thing after stopping.

creak (krēk), **1** to make a squeaking sound. **2** a sharp sound.

cru el (krü' əl), causing pain or unhappiness.

D d

dash (dash), to run quickly.

deal (dēl), to bargain with.

deck (dek), a platform which forms a floor in a ship.

deed (dēd), an act; something done.

de light (di līt'), **1** to please greatly. **2** a feeling of joy.

de mand (di mand'), to ask for without delay.

des ert (dez' ərt), an area of land having little or no water, trees, and plants.

drift (drift), to be carried along by a current of water, wind, or air.

du ty (dü' tē or dyü' tē), the thing which a person should do.

E e

ea gle (ē' gəl), a large bird noted for its great strength.

en gine (en' jən), a machine that gives power to make something work.

en ter (en' tər), **1** to go into; to come into. **2** to begin; to start.

ex cuse (ek skyüz'), to forgive; to pardon.

F f

fail (fāl), **1** to be unable to do. **2** to be of no use when needed.

fa mil iar (fə mil' yər), **1** well-known. **2** well acquainted.

fault (fôlt), **1** a mistake or failing. **2** a responsibility for blame.

fig ure[1] (fig' yər), a shape or form.

fig ure[2] (fig' yər), to think or decide.

hat, āge, fär; let, ēqual, tėrm; it, īce; hot, ōpen, ôrder; oil, out; cup, put, rüle; ch, child; ng, long; sh, she; th, thin; ᴛн, then; zh, measure; ə represents *a* in about, *e* in taken, *i* in pencil, *o* in lemon, *u* in circus.

free dom (frē′ dəm), the ability to act, say, and think as one wishes.

fuse (fyüz), a safety device that melts and breaks the electrical circuit when the current is too strong.

G g

glass y (glas′ ē), having a steady, fixed stare.

glide (glīd), to move smoothly and easily.

glow[1] (glō), a bright, rich color.

glow[2] (glō), to look excited or eager.

guard (gärd), to watch over; to keep safe.

guide (gīd), to show the way.

H h

haul (hôl), to move by pulling, dragging, or carrying.

hob by (hob′ ē), an activity that one likes to work at for fun.

hol low (hol′ ō), having nothing inside.

hu man (hyü′ mən), being a person; having the form of a person.

I i

in sect (in′ sekt), a small animal which has a body divided into three parts and which has six legs and sometimes one or two pairs of wings.

in vite (in vīt′), to ask someone to come to a place or to do something.

ir ri ga tion (ir′ ə gā′ shən), the act of supplying land with water.

J j

jaw (jô), the lower or upper bone that together are the framework of the mouth.

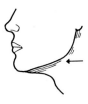

jeans (jēnz), overalls or slacks made from a heavy cotton cloth.

K k

key (kē), a metal device for opening or closing a lock.

kit ten (kit′ n), a baby cat.

L l

la bor (lā′ bər), to work hard.

la zy (lā′ zē), **1** not wanting to work. **2** moving along slowly.

leash (lēsh), a chain or line for keeping an animal under control.

list (list), a written account of names, numbers, words, or phrases.

M m

maid (mād), a female servant.

map (map), a drawing of the whole or part of an area.

mar ket (mär′ kit), a place where goods may be bought and sold.

mead ow (med′ ō), a flat piece of grassland often used as a pasture.

mem ber (mem′ bər), someone or something belonging to a group.

N n

nar row (nar′ ō), not wide; thin.

neat (nēt), **1** clever. **2** orderly and clean.

neph ew (nef′ yü), a son of one's sister or brother; a son of one's sister-in-law or brother-in-law.

nib ble (nib′ əl), to take quick, small bites.

O o

oak (ōk), a tree or shrub found in North America having nuts called acorns.

hat, āge, fär; let, ēqual, tėrm; it, īce; hot, ōpen, ôrder; oil, out; cup, pùt, rüle; ch, child; ng, long; sh, she; th, thin; ŦH, then; zh, measure; ə represents *a* in about, *e* in taken, *i* in pencil, *o* in lemon, *u* in circus.

ought (ôt), to have a duty.

ov en (uv′ ən), an enclosed place used for baking, heating, or drying.

o ver coat (ō′ vər kōt′), a heavy coat worn over indoor clothing in cold weather.

P p

pale (pāl), **1** lacking in color. **2** not bright.

pleas ant (plez′ nt), friendly.

po lite (pə līt′), acting in a proper manner.

pom mel (pum′ əl *or* pom′ əl), the knoblike part of a saddle that sticks up at the front.

R r

rail ing (rā′ ling), a fence made from bars of wood or metal that serves as a guard.

ranch (ranch), a large farm for raising cattle, horses, or sheep.

re al ize (rē′ ə līz), to understand or to think clearly.

re fuse (ri fyüz′), **1** to show an unwillingness to do. **2** to say No to.

re mark (ri märk′), to say in a few words.

S s

scratch (skrach), **1** a small cut. **2** to scrape or rub.

screen (skrēn), a frame covered with wire netting used in a window or door to keep out bugs.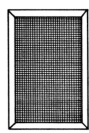

sep a rate (sep′ ə rāt′), to keep or to take apart; to divide.

serv ant (sėr′ vənt), one that waits on another.

shade (shād), a place not in the sunlight.

shud der (shud′ ər), to shake with fear or cold.

T t

tale (tāl), **1** a story. **2** a lie.

task (task), a piece of work that is often hard to do.

traf fic (traf′ ik), the movement of people or vehicles through an area.

treas ure (trezh′ ər), a thing that is greatly loved or valued.

U u

ug ly (ug′ lē), unpleasant to look at.

u ni form (yü′ nə fôrm), the clothes worn by members of a group which help to identify them.

V v

vain (vān), taking too much pride in one's looks or ability.

van ish (van′ ish), to disappear.

W w

weight (wāt), the amount that a person or thing weighs.

wharf (hwôrf), a raised area built along the shore so that ships may load and unload.

whirl (hwėrl), to turn around quickly.

hat, āge, fär; let, ēqual, tėrm; it, īce; hot, ōpen, ôrder; oil, out; cup, pu̇t, rüle; ch, child; ng, long; sh, she; th, thin; TH, then; zh, measure; ə represents *a* in about, *e* in taken, *i* in pencil, *o* in lemon, *u* in circus.

(Acknowledgments continued from page 2.)

Collins + World Publishing Company for "How the Necklace Was Found." Adapted from THE STOLEN NECKLACE by Anne Rockwell. Reprinted by permission of Collins + World Publishing Company from THE STOLEN NECKLACE by Anne Rockwell. Copyright © 1968 by Anne Rockwell.

Doubleday & Company, Inc., for the poem "Only My Opinion" from GOOSE GRASS RHYMES by Monica Shannon. Copyright 1930 by Monica Shannon Wing. Reprinted by permission of Doubleday & Company, Inc.

E. P. Dutton & Co., Inc. for "The Friendly Ghost." Adapted from the book SPOOKS AND SPIRITS AND SHADOWY SHAPES by Elizabeth Yates. Copyright, 1949, by E. P. Dutton & Co., Inc., publishers, and used with their permission.

Nancy Garber for "Raccoons Are for Wild." Adapted from "Raccoons Are for Wild." Copyright © 1973. Published originally in WEE WISDOM magazine. Adapted by permission of Nancy Garber.

"How the Rhinoceros Lost His Smooth Skin" is adapted from the story "How the Rhinoceros Got His Skin" by Rudyard Kipling.

Alfred A. Knopf, Inc. for "Jimmy Takes Vanishing Lessons." Adapted from JIMMY TAKES VANISHING LESSONS, by Walter R. Brooks. Copyright © 1950 by Walter R. Brooks. Reprinted by permission of Alfred A. Knopf, Inc.